Fabulous
FOREPLAY

Other books by Dr Pam Spurr

Fabulous FOREPLAY

The Sex Doctor's Guide to Teasing and Pleasing Your Lover!

DR PAM SPURR

JR
BOOKS

To Nick, the man I love with all my heart

First published in Great Britain in 2007 by JR Books, 10 Greenland Street, London NW1 0ND www.jrbooks.com

A catalogue record for this book is available from the British Library.

ISBN 978 1 906217 05 1

5 7 9 10 8 6

Printed in the UK by CPI Bookmarque, Croydon, CR0 4TD

Contents

Acknowledgements

I'm extremely lucky in that I come across a wide variety of people in both my professional and personal lives. Human nature and behaviour never cease to amaze me. We can learn so much from the lives of others. Many thanks to all of those people who've spoken honestly and openly to me.

I'd also like to acknowledge my gratitude to Jeremy Robson. A fantastic publisher and man to work with.

Finally I'd like to acknowledge the patience of my wonderful children while I've been writing this book.

Safer sex message

Each and every sexually active adult needs to take responsibility for their sexual health and wellbeing. This means being informed about safer sex methods and using them. As the author of *Fabulous Foreplay* I cannot be held responsible for ensuring that when you try the sex techniques in my book that you do so safely.

There's a wealth of sexual health information available to you, and at the end of this book I have listed some websites concerned with safer sex and sexual health. I'd love you to enjoy seducing someone (a lover, new or old) and to give them the most fabulous foreplay, but please do so armed with knowledge to keep yourself safe.

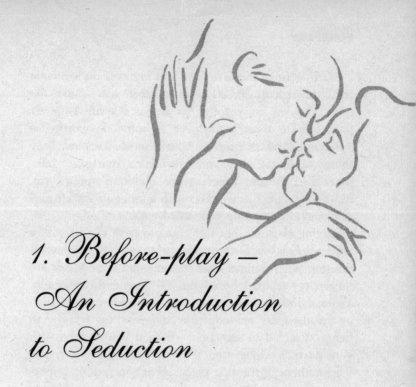

1. Before-play – An Introduction to Seduction

Whether you're in a relationship, you're single, or have just met someone new, you need to know about seduction and foreplay. Both are essential to a pleasurable and fulfilling sexual relationship. It may come as a surprise that I'm talking about seduction for people already in an established relationship. Believe me, this applies just as much to you as to singles and new lovers.

Much of what lies behind dissatisfaction in a couple's sex life is due to the fact that they've forgotten how to seduce each other. They are often guilty of skipping foreplay altogether – instead going straight to the already established pleasure zones that once turned on their partner but which may no longer do so. I aim to revive the neglected art of seduction!

Starting from the first time you lay eyes on someone right through to 10, 20 or even more years down the road, the key to keeping an active sex life is never forgetting to treat your lover as someone worthy of seduction. And as someone who deserves foreplay. Easy things to forget once you've added a mortgage, bills, household chores, career moves, children, in-laws, etc, to what was once new lovers with a fabulous sex life and only each other to be concerned with.

Having clarified that I'm going to treat it as if you're reading *Fabulous Foreplay* with fresh eyes regardless of whether you're single, have recently met someone or are in a partnership, I hope you will treat it this way too. When I introduce certain ideas and techniques − such as my thoughts on seduction and concepts relating to being attracted to someone − even if you've been with your partner a long time, it'll help remind you why you fell for them in the first place. That's incredibly important because at this point in time you may be looking at them with rather jaded eyes − and that's not seductive or sexy. With that in mind, let's begin with the background to seduction.

Before-play

In coming chapters I'll share with you a huge variety of techniques to tease and please your lover with and stimulate their six sexual senses. I'm going to give you a unique way of looking at foreplay and seduction by showing you how each one of these wonderful senses − including the sixth sexual sense that I'll introduce you to − plays an important part in sexual enjoyment. But first let's take a look at the term I coined a number of years ago called 'Before-play'. This is terribly important as it sets the whole scene, establishes the entire background, for how you feel about seducing someone. In my many roles of agony aunt, sex advisor, life coach and psychologist, I came to realise that people get hung up on having sex with little thought to the whole feeling, energy and ambience of their relationship specifically and life generally.

Whether you're aiming to seduce someone new or you want to have sex with your long-term partner, Before-play is important to your success and enjoyment. Here are a couple of examples to illustrate this.

Example One: You've just met someone new and you're looking forward to the exciting date you've got planned tonight. Just as you're about to leave the office, your manager throws a file on your desk and says you've got to complete the work in it before you leave. As you've recently missed a few deadlines you feel you must do as the manager asks. This leaves you rushing late to the date without any time to freshen up or change your clothes. You arrive feeling stressed and overwhelmed with the pressure you've just been under. Do you think you're likely to make scintillating conversation? Are you going to flirt in a carefree manner? And will you be focused on this new person's life and interests? The answer to all three of those questions is a big fat 'No!'

Example Two: You and your partner had a big argument in the morning before leaving for work about an unpaid credit card bill. You're extremely angry with him or her for overlooking it and now the interest has to be paid on it. You're both already strapped for cash and this makes you fume. You tear into each other instead of working together on such matters. That night your partner wants to make amends and slyly thinks a good way would be to have 'make-up' sex and tries to seduce you. Are you in the mood for sex? Do you even want them to touch you? Again the answer is a big fat 'No!'

What Do These Illustrate?

That Before-play is important. That the way you're feeling and any aspect of your life can affect Before-play. These examples demonstrate the ways that very different things in your life can affect your sex life. Quite frankly, if you're stressed from work you're hardly going to make a good impression on a hot new date. Or if you're arguing over bills you're not going to look at your partner with lust. These are only two of thousands of potential examples I could give you to illustrate why people need to think about Before-play. And the fact that Before-play comes into action long before you seduce anyone or start engaging in foreplay.

The Sex Doctor's Prescription For Feeling Fabulous

What arouses you? Knowing how your body responds is terribly important when it comes to foreplay. Lie back in a warm candlelit bath or snuggle down between soft, warm sheets. Close your eyes and gently stroke your breasts/chest, abdomen and thighs. No genital caressing yet!

What to Consider in Your Before-play Zone

Think of Before-play as a pleasurable, comforting and positive 'zone' that you exist in. It directly affects you – and if you're in a relationship it also affects your partner. Just as their Before-play zone affects you. It makes all the difference to feelings of lust and love towards another person – no matter how attractive and new. When it comes to seducing someone and enjoying foreplay, it's definitely a deciding factor. And it holds the key to whether or not you feel any desire or arousal. Here are the major things you should consider that will affect your Before-play zone.

Your Relationship

Any stresses and strains in your relationship will affect your Before-play zone or 'BPZ'. These may be ongoing differences or something that's just flared up. It could be that you disagree about how to spend your weekend, whose family to visit, how much money should be spent on your new kitchen, who does what around the house, or if you dislike your partner's best friend. Your BPZ will also be affected by much more subtle differences. For example, it could be that one of you feels slightly neglected by the other or thinks that they put more into the relationship. Any little irritant or major crisis that isn't acknowledged and dealt with will affect whether or not you have an interest in seduction, foreplay and sex.

Your Work and Other Responsibilities

Your relationship may be solid and loving, or you may be single and interested in someone new, but if your work or other responsibilities are causing you problems, they will affect your BPZ. Don't underestimate the power that work issues have to permeate every aspect of your emotional life, in turn having an impact on your BPZ. Whether it's work or some other major responsibility that takes up your time and energy, you need to recognise the negative effects it can have as illustrated in the example given above.

Your Health

People are surprised when I ask about their physical health when discussing their sex life. All sorts of subtle and not-so-subtle things affecting your health will have a direct impact on how much you want to meet someone new, how much you desire your partner, and how you are around them – sexy, seductive or a big turn-off and not interested anyway. Obviously, any disease or medical problem – a heart problem, diabetes, even a broken leg – will affect your mood. Also, there are side effects of medication that affect sexual arousal and desire. Even if you're simply under the weather you're not going to give out a very positive love-vibe when you go to a singles event. Or if the only thing you want from your partner is a hot drink and a hug – not fabulous foreplay or even a seductive look.

Your Lifestyle

The lifestyle you lead can have anything from very subtle effects on your BPZ to very obvious effects. The easiest way to illustrate this is to think about a man who has drunk too much and gets classic 'brewer's droop' – no matter how much he wants sex he can't get an erection to have it. That's an extremely obvious example but any lifestyle choice will affect your BPZ. If you smoke, drink too much, are overweight, party till dawn and don't get enough sleep, or get stressed over things – these are all lifestyle choices that change the way you feel and act towards your love-interest.

Your Children (If You Have Them)

There's practically no greater potential passion-killer than having children. Yes, children are amazing – I have two myself and I love being a mother. But you must expect your Before-play zone to be severely interrupted if you've children of any age, particularly under-5s. Anyone who becomes a parent should not be ignorant of the fact that children affect every level of your life. Your emotional state and energy levels are particularly affected, and consequently your level of sexual interest and ability to create a positive BPZ.

The Sex Doctor's Prescription For Feeling Fabulous

Make a date with yourself – and if you have a partner, with them also – to go out and have some carefree fun. See a romantic film, join a dance class, go on the swings in your local park! Letting go will enhance your BPZ.

Awareness Equals Action

You're now aware of the type of things that can affect your Before-play zone and this means you can take action. Of course it might be that there's an issue somewhere in your life that can't be sorted out quickly. Also, new issues arise all the time – that's part of life. But the important and positive thing to do is to discuss matters with your partner, if you have one. Or if you're single and aware of ongoing issues, then you won't let these things get on top of you when you're meeting new people. Awareness means your BPZ will be far less affected. Whether it's a piece of action you take to sort out a specific issue, or something ongoing that you simply need to learn to live with (but live with in a positive way), it's how you deal with the matter that decides whether or not it affects your feelings of sexual interest, drive, desire and arousal, which in turn affect how you seduce someone and enjoy foreplay.

Being aware of your Before-play zone, and enhancing and nurturing it, are the very first steps to seduction and fabulous foreplay. Every day, develop an awareness of your life, what's happening in it, what you put into it and how you make others feel. The more aware you are of every level of your life – and the way these levels interact – the better you'll be at arousing someone's interest and being aroused yourself.

This awareness means you're ready to think about whom you are attracted to and how you can attract and seduce their six sexual senses. Let the seduction begin!

2. Attraction and Sexual Chemistry — The Background to Foreplay

It's time to take a look at the very beginnings of seduction and foreplay, and that's all about feeling attracted to someone or finding out that someone finds you attractive. You might think, why bother with this? My reasoning is that if you want to enhance your seduction skills — and be in with a chance to enjoy fabulous foreplay with someone — it's important to understand what's going on behind the intricate processes of attraction and seduction.

With a constant stream of studies about human attraction in the press I won't be surprised if you're a little confused about how to attract someone and how to tell if someone's attracted to you, wondering what are the right and what are the wrong things to do and signals to give when first meeting someone.

It's also part of human curiosity to wonder why we sometimes feel an instant attraction to someone. For example, what was it about one man or woman who stood out at a party that gave you a sense of wanting to meet them? Or why did you lock eyes with one colleague rather than another at a conference?

While sometimes you can be surprised by the fact you've been working alongside a colleague for six months and one day look at them with completely fresh eyes, realising you find them sexy. It can also take you aback to find out that someone's attracted to you when you thought they weren't interested.

There are so many different aspects to human attraction that I'm going to tease out some useful concepts from what might feel like a minefield. It's important to consider alongside these concepts that the timing of meeting someone, the circumstances in which you meet them, your frame of mind and their frame of mind, etc, all go to influence the eventual outcome – whether you end up seducing them and go to bed together.

If you're in a relationship the following might be a healthy reminder of why you fell for your lover in the first place. A very important thing! Research shows that couples who remember their early days are less likely to break up as those happy memories help them get through difficult times – which might include a time when you have, for instance, lost interest in sex.

The Sex Doctor's Prescription For Feeling Fabulous

Believe in what you have to offer! Take a moment to look at yourself in a mirror. Use 'kind and gentle' eyes. What do you really like about yourself? Describe your good points to yourself. This is your private moment to make yourself feel good.

The Elements of Attraction

I'd like to break down the elements of attraction into what I think are logical points. The following areas should become clear as you read them. Even if you choose not to use categories like these for yourself, having an awareness of these things will help you understand why it is that you may or may not end up with someone.

Hot Bodies and Lustful Looks – The Physical Side of Attraction

Most people think attraction is a purely physical event. In one way this view is correct. The very first time you see someone you absorb a huge amount of information about their physical attributes in just a minute or two. We make up our minds pretty quickly whether or not that physical package attracts us instantly or not.

But attraction can grow as we notice more subtle things about a person. You initially take in, say, how tall they are, the colour and style of their hair, their body shape, as well as the style of clothes they are wearing. Then you add to this what their body language tells you. Subconsciously or consciously you might register things such as that they hold themselves in a confident way, they look relaxed and laugh a lot, they seem to be the centre of attention with all eyes on them, or the opposite of these things.

What's interesting is the interaction between absolute physical attributes and the signs and signals you pick up from someone else's body language. Let's say you're a woman who doesn't tend to go for short men. You're out with a friend and notice a man who's about five foot six – shorter than average. Your 'lust-interest radar' goes into neutral mode because he hasn't immediately grabbed your attention by being the six-foot strapping man you normally choose. Out of the corner of your eye you notice, though, how all his friends gather round him and listen to the stories he tells. You notice his confidence and personal energy. He then looks at you, smiles briefly and you think to yourself, 'He's rather attractive for a short man.' And who knows where it will go from there?

Survival of the Fittest

Once we've registered someone's physical attributes and body language, what happens next? Your subconscious mind goes into overdrive. This is because the elements of you being attracted to someone, or not, are rooted in your evolutionary biology. The whole point of men and women getting together in terms of evolution was to make babies and propagate the species. Of course, some men are attracted to men and some women are attracted to women, but that aside, essentially attraction evolved to ensure people mated.

As the millennia have passed, the ways people seduce each other and the rules of attraction may have altered due to the social attitudes of different generations. However, we still can't escape the fact that, at a biological level, certain physical attributes attract us. This mechanism helps to ensure the survival of the fittest.

What Men Look For

Men will immediately register the reproductive health of a woman, whether they know it or not. Subconsciously, they notice the physical signs of good reproductive health, including a youthful face with healthy teeth, wide doe-like eyes, a nipped-in waistline, full hips, and full and high breasts. These physical attributes signal a healthy woman of child-bearing age.

What Women Look For

At a subconscious level, women register a man's physical attributes such as his shoulders being wider than his waistline (the classic V shape), firm buttocks and muscle tone, as well as stature. Again, these signal at a subconscious level that he's a good potential mate for her and a father for her offspring.

That said, many people are attracted to and aroused by specific individual attributes. One man might be a 'breast man', attracted to any breasts or a specific type, such as small and pert ones, or large and round breasts, while another man might be a 'leg man'. One woman might be attracted to a muscular, stocky, testosterone-fuelled physique, while another might prefer a slender man.

Add to this the fact that other aspects alter how you might normally feel about someone. For example, a woman's attraction to a man might be affected by the different stages of her menstrual cycle. Some research suggests that women are attracted to more masculine types during the period of ovulation, and as their cycle nears their point of menstruation they are more attracted to men with softer features.

Opposites Attract

There are further complications in store, though. Because at a subconscious level we are also attracted to, or repelled by, things such as a person's unique smell given off by that individual's specific body chemistry. We register this at a subliminal level and don't even realise we may be attracted or repelled by someone's personal body odour. Again, in evolutionary terms this is fairly important. Research has found that when it comes to our Major Histocompatibility Complex (MHC), whose molecules determine some aspects of our immune response, that we're programmed to be attracted to someone with a differing set of MHC molecules. If we mate with them it helps to ensure our offspring have a greater chance of immunity to a variety of things.

As I'm simply trying to highlight to you how complex human attraction is, I'm not going to give you a full lesson in biochemistry here. But I hope this at least gives you a little taste of the things that might be at play, which you may not even realise when you're attracted to someone, or they're attracted to you, or ideally you're both attracted to each other.

The Sex Doctor's Prescription For Feeling Fabulous

Make your nipples the focus of fabulous sensations. Close your eyes and using a lubricant or massage oil, gently stroke them in circles. Take time to enjoy what might be a new feeling – particularly if you're a man. Alternate the circling with a gentle pinching and squeezing. You'll be able to take this technique into foreplay with your lover.

Your Psyche Is Speaking to Their Psyche – The Emotional and Psychological Side of Attraction

Now we get to the truly complicated and interesting part of attraction – your emotional and psychological make-up and how it affects the way you respond to others! And vice versa. You may spot the man or woman who's physically perfect in your eyes and yet still may not be attracted to him or her once you meet them. This is because both of your personalities begin to interact.

Your Personal History

Frequently we're attractive to people who turn out to be very similar to our main parent of the opposite sex. Often we don't recognise this until we're into a relationship where, for instance, a woman suddenly realises that the man she's been seeing has many personality traits that are the same as her father has. The same is true for men who end up 'marrying their mother'. This is because usually, at a largely subconscious level, we're attracted to people who seem 'familiar'. They seem to share a common ground even if we can't quite put our finger on what that common ground is. Once you're deeper into a relationship it's often easier to see how the qualities of the once most significant man or woman in your life (your father or mother) are what you seek out in a sexual partner. This has nothing to do with incest but everything to do with what we're used to in terms of how we relate to others.

Your Expectations

Sometimes our sexual choices – and whom we find attractive – are very much about our expectations. On the whole, we as humans are very quick to stereotype – and we stereotype as much in our romantic situations and choices as in any other situation or choice. With stereotyping comes a certain set of expectations. A good example is a woman who likes what she thinks of as 'powerful' men. She expects that the manager of a company or a successful lawyer is going to be a powerful man – the type she's attracted to. This sets up a number of expectations when she meets someone. If, on meeting a man at a cocktail party, she's told he's a lawyer or company manager, she then starts to expect that he's got a powerful personality. In her personal set of expectations, power = sexual chemistry and attraction. She then sets about flirting with him despite the fact he may be blond and if she was asked to fill in a questionnaire about physical attributes she'd say she likes brown-haired men. Right now her expectations, based on her emotional and psychological make-up, are in operation and overriding her basic attraction to physical attributes. Of course, the reverse might happen – that's the nature of attraction and seduction!

Your Comfort Zone

An important thing to consider for anyone who's attracted to someone and wants them to reciprocate those feelings is establishing a comfort zone. First off, think of the people we've all heard say that 'an attraction has grown on them' and suddenly they find themselves thinking sexually about what was once a friend. This experience is what I call the comfort zone effect. Two such people have been relating either at work or socially in a group of friends. They've enjoyed the same things or worked on the same projects. Common ground has developed from a small area to many areas. And with this they've developed a comfort zone – they feel comfortable with each other – and at some point this crosses over into attraction. Put simply, we are attracted to people who make us feel good in their comfort zone.

I'll describe how you can apply your comfort zone when you first meet someone you're attracted to in the next chapter, on fabulous flirting.

The Sex Doctor's Prescription For Feeling Fabulous

Sit back, relax and replay in your mind the last time you enjoyed flirting with someone, or enjoyed a date with someone new, or a happy moment with your partner. What made you feel good about this encounter? Hold on to this feel-good memory for a few minutes.

When Rational Thought Comes into Play – Your Basic Needs and Attraction

Seduction isn't always about sexual attraction, lust, expectations and/or romantic love, etc, as sometimes it's a completely rational process. This usually takes two forms. Either you're an extremely objective and rational person when it comes to relationships, as well as other areas that most of us try to be rational about, like our careers. Or you come to a time in your life where you think, 'It's now or never, I've got to find somebody to settle down with and have that family I've always longed for.' This happens to both men and women.

Then the process of looking for a potential partner to seduce, and enjoy a relationship with, becomes much more businesslike. A person in this situation thinks about the basic requirements they want in a potential lover and then sets about finding this person, often through a dating agency. All of the foreplay techniques and tips in coming chapters will apply as much to a person in this situation as any other. You still have to seduce someone and make them feel fabulous!

Are You an Intuitive or Objective Seduction Type?

Apart from those specifically setting out to meet a person with certain requirements, as described above, I find people tend to fall into two main types of seducer: the Intuitive Seducer and the Objective Seducer. This has implications which you should consider for your sex and love life. Work through my quick checklist to find out whether you basically approach seduction intuitively or objectively. Read each question carefully and answer honestly, and if it doesn't seem to apply to you, still choose the answer you think suits you and your attitudes best. Check the key beneath for guidance.

Seduction Checklist

1. Do you have a strong preference for the same physical type?
   Yes/No

2. Are you sceptical about 'love at first sight'?
   Yes/No

3. Even if first impressions are *not* that fantastic, do you give someone another chance?
   Yes/No

4. People aren't necessarily sexually compatible or incompatible – sometimes it's something that has to be worked on. Do you agree with this statement?
   Yes/No

5. Do you think non-verbal communication is fairly *irrelevant* to seducing someone?
   Yes/No

6. Do you approach pursuing a lover much like pursuing any other goal?
   Yes/No

7. Do you think it's an 'urban myth' that there's a true, great love for every person?
   Yes/No

Four or more 'No' Answers = The Intuitive Seducer Type

Choosing mainly 'No' answers means you're likely to be an intuitive type when it comes to the process of seduction, whether you're a man or woman. You probably have a romantic outlook when it comes to seduction, sex and relationships. You believe in a 'great love'. Although, that said, when it comes to how you conduct and choose your relationships you're very likely to have more than one great love in your life, fulfilling different needs at any given time.

You look for an instant chemistry and probably think first impressions are very important – because first impressions tell you this person is sexy, hot and fabulous. However, you probably don't have a particular physical type because, being a romantic, all sorts of people appeal to you for different reasons. For example, you might come across a 'dark horse' and feel the urge to dig deeper. Another time you may be attracted to a very flamboyant person and love the limelight that goes with their outgoing character. You simply go with the chemistry of the moment. You're likely to believe that people are either sexually compatible or incompatible. This is a romantic notion that often goes hand-in-hand with people acknowledging the importance of first impressions and that you can be swept off your feet by sexual chemistry. That is partly true – you may be swept away but don't get stuck in the trap of believing that if you haven't felt an instant attraction it won't come. Often these things build up.

When you believe there's sexual chemistry with someone, you'll throw yourself into foreplay hoping it'll be everything you dream of. Don't place too high expectations on seduction and foreplay.

It's also important to be careful you don't write off someone who doesn't immediately spark sexual attraction in you. And don't get swept away with the romance of a new situation just in case that new lover isn't looking for the same things as you are.

Four or more 'Yes' Answers = The Objective Seducer-Type

Whether male or female, choosing mainly 'Yes' answers suggests you're likely to be an objective type of seducer. You probably have a physical type that you're attracted to and might be rather blinkered to other types. This is because it's likely that a certain physical type has 'floated your boat' in the past and so you tend to stick to it – it's a pragmatic view that this type has been of sexual interest and success for you previously.

That said, you're not swept away by first impressions, instead thinking things through objectively. If things don't work at first, but you can recognise good qualities in a new lover, you're likely to be objective about it and give them another chance. Your sex and love life aren't dictated by romantic notions such as there's only going to be one great love for you. In that sense, you're quite open-minded. You have the type of common sense that tells you that sexual compatibility doesn't necessarily happen overnight.

You might want to break free of the type you tend to prefer and let go a little if you're overly objective about things. As you don't take non-verbal communication too seriously, it might be a good idea to listen more to your intuition when you first meet someone new.

What Happens When an Objective Seducer Crosses the Path of an Intuitive Seducer?

On the positive side, when an objective seducer and an intuitive seducer meet they can bring out complementary qualities in each other. They show the other person another side to seduction, foreplay, sex and relationships. Sometimes, though, the objective person will tire of the romantic notions of the intuitive type.

And vice versa – the intuitive person will wonder why their lover can't let go and be more romantic and less pragmatic in their love life.

These are some of the elements of attraction that form the first stepping stones you cross when you meet someone new. If you're already in a relationship I hope these points will open your eyes to why you and your lover behave in certain ways.

Before I tackle the six sexual senses, let me give you a mini-lesson to turn you into a Fabulous Flirt. Once again, this is as important for singles as it is for couples who need to refresh their flirting and seduction skills before giving each other fabulous foreplay.

3. Fabulous Flirting

Doesn't it feel fantastic when someone gives you a flirty smile, a cheeky glance or a witty compliment? Flirting makes the world a place that's more fun, a little bit exciting, and more sparkling. In my experience, people who can flirt well have a good chance of flirting someone into bed. When you think about it, the same sort of skills are involved in flirting as in foreplay. The only qualitative difference is that flirting tends to be non-physical (although there may be a little touching involved, say of the forearm when talking flirtatiously) while with foreplay things definitely get physical. Essentially, though, flirting and foreplay are about making your lover – and yourself – feel desirable and aroused.

This chapter will give you some key tips, tricks and techniques to help you become a fabulous flirt. Once your flirting skills are honed they will definitely enhance your foreplay skills. If you're presently in a relationship, then by far the majority of this chapter applies to you too. Far too many couples complain to me that the sparkle has gone out of their relationship. Learning to flirt again with someone you love, but perhaps have been neglecting, will drag your relationship out of even the most boring rut.

What's the Point of Flirting?

The main point of flirting is to connect you to potential lovers and partners. A great flirt makes opportunities happen by drawing people into his or her life when they cross paths. Flirting also generally uplifts the feelings of those people around the flirt. And it's just plain fun!

The Initial Phases of Flirting

As soon as someone sets eyes on another person and thinks they're attracted to them – or might be attracted to them (after all, let's give people more of a chance than the very first impression!) – that's when the initial stages of flirting can begin. Getting someone's attention and keeping it is the goal. How do you do this? By laying the groundwork for a Positive Flirt Approach (PFA).

Positive Flirt Approach Tips

★ Make good eye contact but don't sustain it for more than a few seconds or it could be perceived as threatening rather than seductive.

★ Then go for the second and third glance. A second glance hints to the person that you're interested and the third glance definitely gives them a positive flirt signal.

★ Relax your posture towards the person. It's no good shifting your body away from them or if you stop glancing at them.

★ Now it's time for a smile. It could be a flicker of a grin rather than a big, broad smile, but even that's enough to make them confident that they're reading your signals correctly.

★ Next develop your body language further. A woman can cross her legs towards a man and also place her fingertips along her collarbone and upper cleavage. These actions give out signals of her attraction to the man's subconscious mind.

★ A man should pull himself upright and give a subconscious signal of his masculinity through his broad chest and shoulders turned directly towards a woman.

★ To approach or not to approach? On the whole, by making good eye contact, giving repeated glances, a flirtatious smile and positive body language, a woman increases her chances of a man approaching her if she doesn't feel like making the first move. Men should take notice of her signals to make an approach. However, I can't stress enough the many hundreds of men I've met in my work who have told me how much they would welcome an approach made by a woman.

The Signals to Avoid Giving

Just as you can give flirtatious signals that improve your chances of getting into a PFA (Positive Flirt Approach) situation, it's also possible to ruin your chances. Here are some definite no-nos when it comes to body language signals:

★ Prolonged staring at someone is disconcerting and will make them turn away from you.

★ Fidgeting and nervous, jerky movements give the message that you lack confidence, which in turn suggests that you lack sexual chemistry and confidence.

★ Avoid excessively loud and aggressive behaviour with your friends. Such showing off rarely attracts the object of your desire.

★ Be careful not to close down your body language due to nerves. This includes crossing your legs tightly, crossing your arms over your chest or slouching. Not attractive!

★ Overconfident, arrogant body language, including too much preening, an overly straight posture or a nose-in-the-air type of attitude, can be perceived as quite threatening.

The Sex Doctor's Prescription For Feeling Fabulous

Practice makes perfect when it comes to your body language. Sit in a chair in front of your bedroom mirror. Pretend you're rehearsing for a role. First, 'play' at being tense and anxious and show this through your body language. Then 'play' at being confident and flirtatious – what body language do you use? Learn from this experience. We humans are actually very good at using our body language as a powerful tool when we allow ourselves to!

Taking and Making Opportunities

You can enhance your chances of having PFA opportunities by making and taking them. It's important to be prepared for spontaneous encounters – in a lift at work, at a conference, in a pub, at your local grocery shop, etc. Aside from meeting a potential lover at work, or being introduced to one by friends, the main way people meet each other is spontaneously and unexpectedly.

You can take potential opportunities by being aware of who's around you. Walking around with your head in the clouds means you could walk right past people who may be looking straight at you and feeling attracted to you. Likewise, walking around feeling insecure and tense means you close yourself down and don't notice others who might be interested.

How to Be Prepared

★ Maintain a relaxed and confident posture wherever you go where you may come across other people – that's a lot of places! Standing in a lift, going to a meeting out of the office, in your local shop, at the gym or evening class, etc.

★ Always be ready to make first eye contact. Observe your surroundings and then, say, look at the person who may be sharing the lift with you. Remember, no staring, though!

★ The next step is simple – just smile at them. If he or she responds with a smile, use your intuition to judge whether or not to start a simple conversation – small talk. If they respond by closing off their body language then you know they're caught up in their own world and aren't interested in making contact. There's everything to gain and nothing to lose with such an interaction.

Once you start making opportunities for yourself, you then have to take them too. Here are a few key strategies to use:

★ Become a 'Yes person' by saying 'Yes' when someone spontaneously asks you for a coffee at your break or a drink after work.

★ Be the first to ask someone new at work out for a coffee or drink.

★ Go to new pubs, restaurants and clubs. By doing this you widen your 'circle of opportunity' as I call it.

★ Along that same theme, try new things and activities and visit new places.

★ Don't rule out talking to someone or flirting with them (!) just because they don't appear to be your usual type.

The Sex Doctor's Prescription For Feeling Fabulous

Spoil yourself with something that'll make you feel good. Book a massage, go to a department store for a makeover, or experiment with some massage oils as you get to know your own body.

Always Be Safe!

While being open to opportunities to meet new people is a fantastic thing, you also need to do so sensibly. Let's say you meet someone at the supermarket checkout. Safe dating means you take their number rather than give yours. When you ring them, withhold your number. If you decide to meet up, then meet somewhere during the daytime and in a public place. Take a friend with you or at least let a friend or family member know where you're going. Agree that you'll ring them when you leave this first date to go home or back to work. Never take anyone home with you or go back to theirs until you trust and know them. Taking such basic precautions is very important.

The Sex Doctor's Prescription For Feeling Fabulous

Buy a fingertip vibrator to continue your self-exploration. Lie back and with lots of lubricant move the vibrator up and down your labia (lips) if you're a woman and around your testicles if you're a man. Enjoy the lovely sensations.

Once You've Got Their Interest

Having got someone interested in getting to know you by saying 'Yes' to new opportunities that come along and flirting with them, what happens next? Unfortunately, it's just as easy to lose someone's interest as it is to gain it. In the first few minutes of chatting someone up they can decide to back off if they don't feel comfortable around you, despite having at first found you attractive. Getting through the very first impression is important but it's the next 10 or 15 minutes that matter.

Your All-Important Comfort Zone

Flirting develops and becomes a success when you've got someone into your personal space and interacting with you. This is the point where your comfort zone becomes all-important. Your comfort zone is a welcoming and warm place to be. When someone realises they feel comfortable with you, they're going to want to have more time with you and to get to know you better. Here are the key elements for creating your comfort zone:

★ Keep your body language relaxed and flirty.

★ Don't be frightened of pauses or hesitations in the conversation. You can help this new person relax by saying something like, 'It's sometimes nerve-wracking to start chatting, isn't it?' You immediately help someone relax by showing a touch of vulnerability yourself.

★ Laugh a lot and keep the conversation light. Beware of asking serious questions too soon. Keeping it simple – by asking things such as how they found this place, what they think of it, and have they lived in the area for long – makes someone feel much more comfortable than being grilled about their opinion on something the government has done.

★ Keep the spotlight on them. Ask him or her straightforward questions and be ready to feed back to them how their answer might apply to your life. For example, if they say that the food in this place is terrible but they came back because it's so near to their office, you can joke that food poisoning is a small price to pay for convenience. You don't have to be a stand-up comedian to make someone smile!

★ Remember that flirting should be fun and light, not heavy and sexually aggressive.

You've now got a few body language secrets and flirt tips to put into action. Now you can also create your very own comfort zone when you bring someone new into your life. If you're in a relationship, now is the time to create a comfort zone when you're around your partner. It's never too late to enhance and improve your relationship this way. You share your life with them and both of you deserve a wonderful loving and flirty feeling when you're around each other.

If you're single, I'm not going to lay down any ground rules about how soon you should be thinking about seducing someone new and introducing them to some fabulous foreplay. That's up to you. What I would say, though, is if you're looking for more than foreplay and sex, then take your time.

Now it's time for us to explore the six sexual senses.

4. Seduce the Sexual Sense of Touch

There's nothing quite so electrifying as the first brush of skin against skin or the tentative whisper of a kiss as lips meet between two lovers. If you're seducing someone new, your heart pounds as you begin to explore each other through touch during your first tentative forays into foreplay. Or if you're long-term lovers who know exactly which erogenous zones to start caressing to arouse your partner, touch is still an important part of fabulous foreplay.

So let's begin with the sense of touch because it seems to fit naturally with seduction and foreplay. Unless you're having cybersex or phone sex, touching is going to be involved at some stage – even if you tease each other with lots of banter and flirting before you actually make physical contact.

As *Fabulous Foreplay* is as much for singles, those in new relationships, and long-term lovers to learn from, every suggestion, technique, trick and tip is aimed at everyone to try, unless I specifically say otherwise. They are equally for male and female readers. Unless I describe something as being just for a man to do, or only for a woman to try, assume either sex can enjoy it.

Similarly, regarding certain techniques that are multi-sensual (meaning they stimulate more than one of your lover's senses), I'm not going to make a point of separating out how each technique can stimulate more than one sense. For example, if you're giving a lover oral sex or kissing their different erogenous zones, not only do you rouse their sense of touch but you also stimulate their sense of hearing with the kissing and licking noises you make. I've tried as far as possible to put techniques within the appropriate sensory chapter but do bear in mind the multi-sensual nature of many techniques.

Throughout *Fabulous Foreplay* I suggest using massage oils, lubricants, sex toys and other items. At the end of the book you'll find many recommended websites where you can browse and shop for these things.

Our sense of touch is essentially the very first sense that's stimulated when we're born. The process of birth, and being immediately handled with loving care, is the first experience of many that form the basis for our initial impressions of our world.

Our skin is absolutely packed with touch receptors and nerve endings. In infancy our mothers, fathers and extended family give us cuddles and physical contact, much-needed for our emotional development. This contact gives us a sense of love, comfort and security.

As we grow into adulthood we continue to enjoy the pleasurable aspect of touch when given the opportunity. We obviously have less affectionate contact with our family. And, ironically, we often experience less touch as we pass through adolescence because physical contact is discouraged by society or not available to us until we're older and meet someone who becomes a romantic or sexual partner.

For many people, this means there are gaps in their life when they don't have much physical contact with anyone. As their sense of touch becomes less stimulated, it becomes less associated with pleasure. And as with anything that's underused, our sense of touch becomes 'jaded' and dull. Sadly, many adults enter relationships that involve too little touch and they may never rekindle the pleasure of this important sensory experience.

However, the good news is that since we are sensitive when it comes to touch, we can 're-stimulate' this sense by other means. Bear in mind, though, that different parts of our body tend to respond more – or less – sensitively to touch. For example, our fingertips are more sensitive than the backs of our hands. The inside of the wrist is more sensitive than the outside of the arm. The back of the knee is more sensitive than the front of the thigh. The inner thigh is more sensitive than the outer thigh, and so on. But these differing levels of intensity in the sense of touch make exploring our own and a lover's body all that much more exciting.

Overall, women have many more nerve endings than men, making their skin inherently more sensitive. This doesn't mean that men don't enjoy touch – they do. But it means that sometimes men are less likely without encouragement to explore a lover's erogenous zones fully and completely.

Re-Stimulate Your Sense of Touch

I'd like you to begin by re-stimulating your own skin before you even begin to think about how to pleasure a lover with touching techniques. There are many ways you can heighten your own sensitivity. Believe me, many people who have been single for a long time or who have had unsatisfactory sexual relationships have a sense of touch that's gone into 'hibernation'. Re-stimulating it is terribly important!

Seduce Your Own Skin

For men and women, it's worth investing in a good body brush and regularly brushing your skin in long, sweeping motions. Not only does this exfoliate your skin, enhancing its appearance, but it'll also help sensitise your skin.

Not everyone enjoys body brushing so you could instead use an exfoliating scrub. There are many body scrubs on the market, aimed at men as well as women. The best way to use them is standing in the bath or shower and gently rubbing the scrub in circular motions around your skin, taking time to go over your whole body.

Waxing also sensitises the skin. Many women have tried leg and bikini waxing, and perhaps waxing other parts of their body. It's also becoming more popular with men. Waxing leaves your skin feeling fresh, invigorated and more sensitive.

Shock Tactics For Your Skin!

Run a warm bath and add delicious scented bath oil or bubbles, if you like. Take a cup of ice cubes and while you enjoy your warm bath, run a piece of ice around different parts of your body. Once it melts, take another and run it along another part of your body. You can circle your nipples, glide it across your abdomen, run it up and down between your inner thighs, over your shoulders, around your knee and behind your knee, and even around your genitals. The contrast with the warm water is invigorating – and shocking – for your skin!

Auto-Sensual Massage

This is self-massage aimed at stimulating your sense of touch and your receptiveness to a lover's touch. Auto-sensual massage simply uses basic massage techniques all over your body in order to increase your receptiveness.

With some lovely scented massage oil, lie back on a big soft towel and begin by massaging one hand with the other. Circle your palm, varying the pressure in order to stimulate your touch receptors. Note how fabulous it feels and what you like most. Then repeat on the other hand.

Repeat circular, stroking and gentle 'pinching' massage movements on different parts of your body. Enjoy this, take your time, and explore what type of touching feels best – and where. The more you learn about yourself the more you'll be able to share this knowledge with your lover. These techniques will also enhance the pleasure you give when touching your lover's body.

Your Own Pleasure Map

Take the auto-sensual massage one step further and use it to arouse yourself sexually. Whether in a warm bath or shower, or between cool sheets in bed, explore your different erogenous zones. Erogenous zones are specifically associated with sensual and sexual pleasure, and vary tremendously between individuals. While one person may love having their neck stroked, giving them tingling sensations all over their body, another person may hate being touched there, or it might simply make them giggle but doesn't feel sensual.

Identify which touch brings a particular erogenous zone to life for you. For example, a woman might find that gently pinching her nipples makes them spring to life but she wouldn't use a pinching technique down her inner thighs. Instead she might find that gently brushing her fingernails up and down her inner thigh gets her aroused.

Remember, these different erogenous zones make up your very own pleasure map. You can enjoy them during self-pleasure and later share them with your lover.

Your Lover's Pleasure Map

It's time to 'pleasure-cise' your lover! Having learned about your own pleasure map, apply this knowledge to discovering your lover's. Tell them you don't want to have full sex but that you simply want to try this 'pleasure-cise' on them.

Have them lie back ensuring they're warm and comfortable. Explain to them this pleasure-cise is about discovering their unique pleasure map. Turn it into a little game and ask them to rate between one and 10 (with 10 being the most pleasurable) the different touching techniques you try around their different erogenous zones. This is NOT about them judging what you do – it's completely about them giving you lots of information about their very own pleasure map. Their pleasure map may be completely different from yours.

Touching Techniques

A misguided assumption people tend to make is to assume that there's just one or two ways of touching someone. There are many different ways you can touch someone. And you can simply vary the pressure of, say, a circular motion with your fingertips. You could do extremely light circles around your lover's nipples and then increase the pressure when making circular motions with your fingertips on their pubic bone.

Don't forget that through the sense of touch your lover may get 'secondary stimulation'. By secondary stimulation I mean that if, for example, you were to gently rub your fingertips back and forth across their pubic bone (or use circular motions as I just described), you might indirectly stimulate the base of a male lover's penile shaft or a female partner's clitoral region. Such secondary stimulation occurs through nerve connections that run right across our body – in this example from the soft skin above their pubic bone to the area lower in their genital regions. This secondary stimulation can sometimes be even more sensual and pleasurable than the actual stimulation itself.

The Sex Doctor's Prescription For Feeling Fabulous

The most important rule of touching is to remember that every lover likes different touching sensations. You'll be considered a fabulous lover if you approach each new relationship like a blank slate, rather than expecting your new lover to enjoy the same types of touch that your last lover did.

Try the following touching techniques. Any of them can be used with or without massage oils or lubricants.

Basic Stroking

Imagine your index and middle finger are drawn together and use the pair of them to move in an upward stroke. You can make little stroking movements or much larger ones. The basic stroke can be used anywhere from stimulating large areas, like the upper back, to much smaller areas, like where a woman's inner thighs meet the outer labia.

Drumming

A fabulous sensation is created by 'drumming'. This is where you alternate drumming with your index and middle fingers. Imagine drumming to be as light as raindrops hitting your skin. Have your lover lie back while you gently tease him or her across their pubic bone and around the base of his shaft, or down her labia, with this very gentle drumming. This technique will create a lot of sexual tension.

Fluttering

This technique is like drumming but uses all of your fingertips. Imagine fluttering them across your lover's neck, breasts, abdomen, buttocks, inside their thighs, around their knees – anywhere that a gentle fluttering will stimulate.

Rubbing

This is a smaller and subtler version of stroking. The best way to visualise it is as a 'sanding' motion where your index and middle fingers rub back and forth in very small movements. Rubbing is fantastic for small erogenous zones such as behind the ear, behind the knee, at the top of the cleft of the buttocks, and on different parts of the genitals. It's fabulous when done with a touch of massage oil or lubricant.

Twirling
For incredibly delicate places use the twirling touch. I can best describe it as if you were very gently twirling a pen between your thumb and index finger. It's incredibly sensual if you pull gently on your lover's skin and twirl back and forth – though it must be done *very* gently. If your lover can take direct clitoral contact, she may like twirling on her clitoris or on her clitoral hood. A man may like it at the base of his testicular sack where the skin is loose.

Circular massage
You can apply a small, circular massage movement with your index, middle and ring fingers across any erogenous zone. This touching technique is particularly good for increasing blood flow to enhance sensation.

The Sex Doctor's Prescription For Feeling Fabulous

If your lover tells you how much they like one touching technique then be sure to give them plenty of that. However, you can overstimulate one area, so don't overdo it. For example, they may love a drumming sensation on their inner thighs right next to their genitals. Take a break from this and stroke their lower abdomen before you go back to giving more drumming sensations there.

Advanced Touching Techniques

Once you start stimulating a lover during foreplay through touch, you can build your repertoire to include some more advanced and sophisticated techniques. Sometimes people are anxious about trying something new or different when touching a lover. The simple solution is to ask if they like the new sensations you're giving them. You don't have to take it to heart if they don't like something you've tried as it's all about sex-perimentation and learning. Some things they'll love and some things they may not like very much. But it's important to get that information when exploring foreplay techniques.

Top Touching Tips

★ Always ensure your hands are warm.

★ Keep asking if the sensation feels pleasurable.

★ Never feel embarrassed to say that something doesn't feel good or has stopped feeling good. Your lover wants to know they're giving you fabulous foreplay.

★ Keep your nails trimmed and hands as soft as possible – calluses don't feel very pleasant when rubbed over a lover's skin!

Try one or two of the following to build up your foreplay confidence.

The V sign – a guaranteed victory!

This is one of the very best techniques for stimulating her clitoris without direct touch. Imagine your fingers are in the traditional 'V' for victory sign with index and middle fingers slightly parted. Slip your index and middle finger down over her pubic bone so they're either side of her clitoris. The pad of your index finger and the pad of your middle finger each rest on one of her outer labia (lips). Rock your hand gently so your V sign strokes up and down her two labia. This generates stimulation of her clitoris by pulling gently on her outer labia, which pull on her clitoral 'arms'. Her clitoris is the little 'bud' visible underneath her clitoral hood, and the clitoral 'arms' are connected through tissue below her clitoris which then runs under the skin of the labia.

Labial Massage

The labial massage is a fabulous touching technique. Your lover should lie back with her legs relaxed. Using your thumb and fingers, gently massage as if you were gently kneading dough. Begin at the bottom of one of her labia and move upwards taking as much time as you like – and as she wants. You need to be ever so gentle to heighten her pleasure. As your fingers massage upwards and you're about to pass around her clitoris, you can pause and gently circle it. Use your favourite lubricant so your fingers can slip gently as they massage.

The Full Four

Allow all four of your fingers to relax down and over her pubic bone. Your fingertips should just be at the entrance of her vagina – the introitus. Again, this is to be done with care and a delicate touch as you stroke, rub or circle with massage movements around this area. As she gets more aroused and lubricated you can allow one or more of your fingers to slip inside her vagina.

Alternating Hands

This technique can be used on any larger area such as the breasts, the buttocks and the inner thighs. Using lots of lubricant or massage oil, place your hands on the area to be massaged and while one hand pushes downwards the other pulls upwards, gently alternating back and forth. In this way your hands pass each other. When massaging the inner thigh you can ensure your finger nearest your lover's genitals gently skims their genitals to tease and arouse them.

Erotic Eight

While your lover is lying on their back you can apply the Erotic Eight technique. This gives them fabulous stimulation of large areas of their body. It is perfect to do with a luscious body massage oil. Starting with your hands together at their breastbone, swirl outwards and under their breasts, or to the sides of their ribcage for a male lover. Then bring your hands together at the point just above their navel. Swirl back outwards along their hips, bringing your hands back together at their pubic bone. You can now see how this makes a figure-of-eight shape. Swirl your hands back up their body coming in just above their navel, then outwards and back up to the top of their breastbone. Repeat the movement, varying the pressure and the speed with which you swirl in and out over their body. This also feels heavenly done on a lover's back and buttocks if they lie on their stomach.

The Sex Doctor's Prescription For Feeling Fabulous

A word of warning to men – don't forget how your facial hair might feel to your lover. Particularly when it comes to oral sex, most women want a smooth and clean-shaven chin. At any point during foreplay – when your face may brush against any part of her – you need to be aware of this.

Penetrative Touch That Feels Fabulous

During foreplay you can use any of the touching techniques above for penetrative touch with a female lover. Timing is important when you're moving from touching the skin of her erogenous zones to touching inside her vagina. Here are the most important considerations:

1. Never rush penetrative techniques. For example, you might be caressing her inner thighs and start running your fingers over her labia – perhaps giving her a labial massage. You can then slip one finger just inside the entrance to her vagina and tenderly move it around, then withdraw it and continue stimulating her labia. This is a perfect point at which to ask her if she wants you to insert your finger back in.

2. Always take care, when running your fingers over her labia and into her vagina, that you get constant feedback from her on how it's feeling.

3. Always begin penetrative touch with one finger, as two or three may cause her discomfort or even pain.

4. Use lots of lubricant to ensure she keeps moist.

5. You'll heighten her arousal if you tell her how much you're enjoying penetrating her.

The Sex Doctor's Prescription For Feeling Fabulous

Why not try 'The Stir' for a fabulous penetration technique? With your index and middle fingers together, insert them slowly and sensually into her vagina. Once your fingers are inside make a 'stirring' motion with them – as if you're stirring a bowl of honey. With a gentle action stir them around and around so that you carefully stimulate her vaginal walls. A much-neglected zone!

Fabulous and Forbidden Touching

More people are getting curious about exploring anal sex. Many find it extremely pleasurable and others don't wish to try it, or on trying it find it uncomfortable. This is a very personal decision and no one should feel pressured to have anal foreplay and sex. If you and your lover are willing to try it, here are some important tips to help make it a more pleasurable experience:

★ Sex-periment a little with some gentle touching of the perineum and anal area. The perineum is located on both men and women running upwards from the anal passage to the opening at the base of the vagina on a woman, and up to the testicular sack on a man.

★ You need to use safer sex practices. For fingering of the anal area, you can slip your finger into a condom or a latex finger cover available from your chemist. When it comes to oral pleasure – as discussed in Chapter 6, seducing the sexual sense of taste – you need to use a dental dam or sturdy clingfilm to prevent transmission of bacteria from the anal area to the mouth.

★ As the anal passage doesn't lubricate itself the way the vagina does, you'll need lashings of condom- or latex-friendly lubricant. Please keep re-lubricating the area.

★ Anal foreplay can involve gentle fingering or 'rimming' – where you use your tongue and lips to stimulate this area through a dental dam or clingfilm.

★ You can stroke, gently massage, kiss and generally play around this area that's highly sensitive. But beware you don't overstimulate the anus as it can get quite sore.

★ If you continue to full penetrative sex, the rectum needs to be empty and the person receiving penetration should expel any trapped wind. An easy way to do this is to slip into the bathroom in private, get down on all fours and tip your pelvis upwards, as wind rises and is more easily expelled in this position!

★ Condoms should always be used during anal penetration.

Fabulous Foreplay and Simple Erotic Pleasures

In my last book, *Sensational Sex: The Revolutionary Guide to Sexual Pleasure and Fulfilment*, I introduced the idea of simple erotic pleasures or SEPs. Where appropriate, depending on which sense you're seducing, I'll outline a few SEPs to use in your foreplay. SEPs involve taking everyday things and turning them into something sensual. Perfect for lovers who have lost that loving feeling and want to rekindle things.

For the sense of touch, here are a few SEPs involving heavenly hair-play to try on your lover.

Scalp massage

A scalp massage feels fabulous and you don't need be a hairdresser to give one. Your partner can lie back in your lap or you can go behind their chair with their head relaxing back. Gently stroke from the top of their forehead back along their scalp to the base of the neck. Repeat this a few times. Next place your fingertips at the top of the forehead again, but with gentle pressure circle your fingertips rather than stroking back over their scalp. You can slowly move up and over their scalp to the base of their neck, pausing while you circle your fingertips for a few moments before moving your hands to restart circling again.

Brushing their hair

It's a real pleasure when someone brushes your hair – a SEP most of us never experience. Standing over your lover, start from the forehead and work backwards, brushing rhythmically and gently. It's terribly relaxing and your lover will feel completely pampered by this.

Washing their hair

Why not offer to wash your lover's hair? It's another SEP most of us never experience unless we're at the hairdresser's. Your lover sits in the bath while you use the showerhead to shampoo them. Glide the shampoo round and round their hair. Rinse with lovely warm water. Be gentle and careful when it comes to combing through wet hair.

Oriental Hair Massage

Gently tease and tantalise your lover's skin with your hair. They should be lying comfortably while you straddle them. Bending over them you can gently swish your hair across their nipples, down their abdomen, over their genitals and anywhere you think they need stimulating. Even a man (or woman with short hair) can give this SEP as the ends of short hair can be just as stimulating to the skin as long, flowing hair.

The Sex Doctor's Prescription For Feeling Fabulous

Try the 'Thai Body Massage' for a really sensual experience. While kneeling over your lover, glide your naked chest or breasts across theirs. Then skim your lower pelvis against theirs. Women can brush their labia against the edge of his penis, and men can swish their erect or even semi-erect penis across her nipples, tummy, thighs and genitals. As a part of foreplay this is incredibly seductive and arousing.

A Few Fabulous Ways to Heighten Sensual Tension

When you seduce your lover's sense of touch, you don't have to use your own fingertips, hands or body to arouse them. There are many other ways you can create sexual tension and heighten their foreplay experience.

Feathering

This is one of the most fabulous foreplay techniques I know and I've been recommending it for years. All you need is a feather (a clean one, obviously!), available from an adult shop or even a crafts store, and some massage oil. Your lover lies back while you drizzle the oil over their skin. Take the feather and gently use the tip to trace circular, back-and-forth or squiggle patterns over their skin through the oil. It's incredibly sensual and heightens your lover's sense of touch.

Sensual Materials

Get creative during foreplay and give your lover new sensations. For example, touch your lover through her silk knickers. It feels fantastic if a man gently uses his fingertips in little up-and-down movements along a woman's labia with the silk between his fingers and her genitals. It increases sexual tension because she knows there's silk between his touch and her genitals.

Complete Seduction of the Sense of Touch

When you think about foreplay and seduction as a complete experience, you need to consider things such as the touch of bedding where you make love. For example, if your sheets are starched and stiff, or old and ragged, they won't feel sensual against you and your lover's skin. But if they're lovely smooth cotton or silky satin they'll enhance your pleasure.

This goes for anything you come into contact with during foreplay – pillows or cushions on your sofa if you seduce your lover in your sitting room, or the feel of the kitchen counters, table or bathroom cabinet if you get frisky in one of those rooms. Always be prepared to throw a comfortable and soft blanket onto something hard like the kitchen table if you're going in for a quick seduction. The same is true for foreplay and seduction alfresco, where you need to be comfortable with a soft blanket below you both and another on top of you for warmth.

A Pleasure-cise to Heighten the Sense of Touch
Take a hairbrush (preferably with natural bristles) and gently brush the fingers and palms of your hands. Use little, circular motions to bring the sense of touch to life on your hands, which are so important to foreplay.

I hope you've enjoyed reading about how to seduce your lover's sense of touch. Of course, everything you do to them, they can do in return to you. The sense of touch is terribly important in intimate relationships as when we stroke, caress and stimulate each other's bodies we release the bonding hormone oxytocin. This deepens our experience of touch specifically, and our experience of lovemaking and relationships generally.

You might wonder why I haven't included various foreplay techniques that are fabulous and involve touch – for example, bondage play, which involves the sense of touch in many ways. There are so many techniques you can use during foreplay that I have spread them across the different chapters for seducing the six sexual senses. For instance, while bondage is often about the feeling of restraint, and sex-play such as spanking and whipping are about taking touch to extremes, they also involve an incredibly visual set of erotic techniques.

So, let's explore the next sexual sense – the fabulous sense of sight.

5. Seduce the Sexual Sense of Sight

Seduction and fabulous foreplay involve every single part of your, and your lover's, world. The sense of sight forms a large part of this world. It's an incredible process and has a paramount place in noticing someone, feeling attracted to them, and in developing lust and sexual desire.

It begins with the very first, exciting few seconds you set eyes on someone and with lightning speed feel a prickle of interest – or not as the case may be. Everyone has experienced that near-instantaneous moment of interest. And in your mind's eye I'd like you right now to pause and think back to the last time you saw someone attractive. In just a few moments you would have registered so much about them and the way they looked. It's well established by research that first impressions like this are terribly important and they have an impact on what we think and feel about what we see. If you like what you see, you want more of it.

Moving this process a few steps further along, there's the moment when you first see a potential lover look back at you in a certain way, perhaps as they get ready to touch you and kiss you for the first time. All the little things in their behaviour, and the way they look at you, plus the way they look physically, are registered through your sense of sight.

It's through this sense that you feel a thrill of sexual arousal as you watch them undress and act flirtatiously or sexily. And it's through sight that many aspects of *where* these moments take place are registered – the lighting, the colours, the atmosphere; sight is so much a part of your pleasure and enjoyment. It helps you absorb and enjoy so much of your sexual experience along with your other senses.

The following include a number of ways to seduce your lover's sense of sight during foreplay. Many of the suggestions will help you enjoy a full and fabulous foreplay experience. Some might surprise you!

Here's Looking at You

Attracting someone new and continuing to attract them once in a relationship is a complex process. The whole thing is initiated by sight – the signs and signals we give out that someone else sees. And the reverse – the signs and signals *we* see in someone else. I've already described a few signs and signals that people give off when first attracted to someone in Chapter 3 on fabulous flirting. But there are other things I'd like you to try that will stimulate your lover's sense of sight. You can also look out for them in a partner or potential lover.

Seductive Signs and Signals a Woman Can Give

★ Signal sexual interest by gently fiddling with a necklace. This draws his eye-line down to your cleavage and the subconscious signal is that you want him to look there.

★ If you are holding a glass, sensually run your finger around the rim of the glass. This signals to his subconscious that you are interested in him.

★ Form a flirty 'S' shape with your figure. For example, while your left hip curves outwards to the left, your right shoulder pushes out to the right, forming a very feminine 'S' line, signalling attraction.

★ Cross your legs and gently circle the foot of your upper leg. Don't jerk it in a fidgety way but instead roll it in a sensual way. This signals your sexual tension (which needs releasing!) to his subconscious mind.

★ Lightly lick your lips before answering a question of his. He'll pick up this incredibly sexy signal.

★ Run your fingers gently through your hair signalling to him that you could touch him in this erotic way. This isn't nervous twirling but soft and sensual stroking.

Seductive Signs and Signals a Man Can Give

★ Tilt your head downwards yet look directly into her eyes. This gives a sense that you are taller and bigger than she is (even if you're actually the same height) and attracts her subconscious mind to this image. A subtle biological clue to attraction has been found in the male–female height ratio, as men are usually taller.

★ If standing beside her, at some point while talking, gently touch her forearm (obviously if appropriate), as this forms a subconscious bond between your two bodies.

★ Facing her square on, hook your thumb into your belt loop or slip your hand into your pocket. This is a subconscious signal of your masculinity (or more literally signalling the area of your manhood) and will attract her if she's interested.

★ Smooth your hair back with one slow and sensual sweep. Not only does this signal your height to her subconscious mind but it also draws attention to your face.

The Sex Doctor's Prescription For Feeling Fabulous

Surprise your lover or the new person in your life and wear something completely different that reflects another aspect of your personality.

Seduce With Colour

Our immediate surroundings have a definite impact on the way we feel. This is true whether you are out and about with someone new or have brought them back to your home. Whether we are consciously aware of it or not, we are affected by the lighting, décor, colour, and the size and shape of a room.

An easy example to illustrate this point is lighting.

Everyone knows what it's like to sit in an office dominated by harsh strip lighting. It makes you feel agitated and on edge. The last thing you want a new lover or an established partner to feel is on edge in your company. With some simple changes to the lighting you can establish a calmer atmosphere.

Another way to illustrate this is the design or style of the room you're in. A small space might make you feel claustrophobic, whereas a large room can make you feel free and relaxed. But get the colour and lighting right and a small space can feel cosy and seductive.

In terms of seduction and the mood you're in, which in turn affects how satisfying your foreplay is, colour may have the most impact of all. You may not be able to control the environment where you first meet or where you first take someone for a date – unless perhaps you take them to a 'romantic' restaurant – but you can control the environment in your home, beginning with the colour scheme.

Colour has an incredible power to alter your mood. We absorb so much colour through our sense of sight but often forget this very key factor in the environment. Here are a few seductive suggestions for changing this aspect of your environment to get the benefits you desire.

The Sex Doctor's Prescription For Feeling Fabulous

Alter the feel of your bedroom simply by using coloured light bulbs. Experiment with the different colours available to see what works best with your colour scheme.

For Sensuality

Choose rich milk-chocolate tones, as well as darker chocolate tones. Deeper shades of red and crimson also enhance sensuality, and deep salmon pink tones lend themselves to sensual moods. Even in a smallish bedroom these colours can make you feel cocooned in sensuality when used carefully.

For a Commanding or Authoritative Effect

If you're into anything like bondage sex-play (coming up soon), use deep purples, dark royal blues and shades of black to enhance a sense of authority and of being in command. These Gothic colour tones give a message of strong sexuality. With subtle lighting you can give a powerful message to a lover without going too over-the-top.

For a Liberating Effect

Some people prefer a more liberating effect through colour. Choose pale turquoises and light, sunny yellows for a liberating feel. The fact that the age-old remedy for a long-term illness was a trip to the seaside to enjoy fresh air, sunshine and turquoise seas indicates just how powerful these colours are held to be. Shades of deeper pink are also liberating, romantic and sensual.

Your Seduction Nest

Keep the notion of a 'romantic' restaurant in mind when decorating your own personal space. It's the lighting, colours, decor, and so on, that make it romantic. It doesn't matter if you're in a long-term relationship or single and enjoying meeting new people, to have a place that makes you feel sensual will add to your seduction experience – and that of your lover.

Once you've settled on an overall colour theme, some simple changes to décor can make all the difference to your 'seduction nest' in the bedroom or your living room. Fabrics, design and lighting are the other key elements in the overall experience of seducing your lover's sense of sight.

To complement your colour theme you can add throw cushions and drape some gorgeous fabrics in a few select places. Such easy tricks aren't costly and even the least creative man or woman only needs a touch of imagination to make these things work.

You and your new lover (or long-term partner) can either enter a plain, drab, cheerless room or one that's decorated in sensual tones with a couple of big, soft colour-toned throw cushions and a yummy soft throw draped across the sofa. Add in a few accessories, such as candlesticks and an exquisite piece of erotic art, and it'll make all the difference to the feel. Finish off with some freshly cut flowers or a beautiful and erotic-looking orchid plant – or both.

The Sex Doctor's Prescription For Feeling Fabulous

Create a new mood in your bedroom – it's quite simple to turn it into an exotic boudoir. For example, you can create an Eastern theme by draping some pashminas here and there, placing a few plump, embroidered pillows on your bed, and putting a few Eastern *objets d'art* (incense burners and bells, say) at critical points in your bedroom.

How Do I Look in This?

The way you look in terms of the clothes you wear makes a powerful impact and gives off messages about your sensuality and sexual chemistry. I've already discussed how first impressions are important in terms of body language signals, but what you wear also carries a powerful message, particularly for the sense of sight. Bright, loud colours will grab someone's attention. Dark colours may switch off a person's attention, unless of course it's a particular style you're going for, like a fetish look.

There are all sorts of sexual messages you can give through the styles you choose. This includes the powerful signals from bondage and fetish gear, while at the opposite end of the spectrum you could go for an innocent and 'virginal' look by wearing white lace – particularly when it comes to women's lingerie.

In between these two extremes, a woman in particular has many choices. Lots of men love the brashness of red and crimson-toned lingerie, or the sexy message of vibrant pinks reflecting the pink of her lips. Then there's the clash of messages you get from, say, sexy stockings teamed with a pale pink knickers and bra set. A man's mind might start wandering – is she giving a message of power and domination through the stockings or one of femininity and submission through the pink underwear?

Some Simple Rules For Looking Sexy

If you're planning to seduce your lover's sense of sight through what you wear, there are a number of things you can do to make sure it's a success.

★ Know your lover's taste – although you might want to slip into an all-black-lace dress, your lover may hate that Gothic look. Stimulating their sense of sight is what it's about, not your personal tastes!

✶ Try before you buy! Just because something looks fabulous on the hanger in the shop doesn't mean you'll feel sexy in it. With any clothing, you should try it on before you buy it, but this is particularly important when it comes to looking and feeling sexy.

✶ Build your body confidence by first wearing your new gear when alone. Turn the lights down low and practise walking around and feeling good in your new things.

It's Not Just For His Eyes

Since men get so turned on by seeing women in sexy gear – as men are so easily stimulated visually – they forget their lover might want to see *them* looking seductive and ready for foreplay. There is now a wide range of gorgeous-looking underwear for men on the market as well as all sorts of fun and sexy items to try; for example, there are genital bondage straps (lots of varieties!) or a slinky thong or one with leather and studs. Don't neglect what you've got on underneath just because you're so focused on the way she looks.

Seduce With Bondage and Fetishism

There are all sorts of adult shops in the high street and websites that sell a vast array of bondage and fetish items. There's practically anything you could dream of. You can't underestimate the visual impact of wearing fetish gear and what an incredibly powerful visual statement you can make. The two most important rules for successfully wearing bondage and fetish gear are:

1. Know your lover's likes and dislikes. A man may love it if a woman puts on a PVC mini-skirt and stiletto heels but hate it if she puts on a lace-up dominatrix cat-suit and boots. That may be a step too far!

2. Be selective and choose one fabulous piece of fetish gear. You don't have to deck yourself from head to toe in it. A really sexy leather corset teamed with a simple black skirt is incredibly seductive. But team that same corset with a leather mini-skirt and over-the-knee fetish boots and it might look too much.

Dressed For Fabulous Foreplay

Now that I've highlighted some rules about making a visual impact, here are some other ideas to stimulate your lover's sense of sight. Remember, the messages contained in the way we dress for a lover make an impact not only on the sense of sight but also at a much deeper level. Don't underestimate the visual effect of high heels, thigh-high boots or stilettos. The sleek and slim lines appeal to the sense of sight and also give a seductive message of femininity coupled with power.

If you and your partner are both into bondage-play, it'll be fun for you to browse through bondage clothing in an adult shop. All that you see can be stimulating and will create a sense of excitement before the foreplay has even started. Or you can get lots of ideas for creating your own bondage-looking gear if you're on a budget. Carefully cut a few strategic peep holes here and there in an ordinary garment for your nipples, vagina or penis to show through, and you'll definitely arouse your partner.

The Sex Doctor's Prescription For Feeling Fabulous

Why not slip on some fabulous, silky black stockings and stiletto heels? They make a powerful visual impact. Stand above your lover and let him unclip your stockings and roll them down while kissing each leg all the way from your inner thigh down to your ankle.

Bound, Gagged and Ready For Foreplay

Not only does bondage gear make a huge visual impact but so too does the paraphernalia that goes with it. There are the ties, sashes, ropes, whips, handcuffs and blindfolds, etc. Just the sight of a riding crop casually slung across a chair will excite some people. Such items can be used to great effect even if you're only into what's called 'vanilla' sex-play – gentle and pretend bondage-play.

As I mentioned in the last chapter on seducing the sexual sense of touch, bondage-play stimulates the sense of touch in a number of ways but due to its powerful potential to make a visual impact, I thought it best to include bondage suggestions in this chapter.

Tease and Tantalise

One of the best aspects of bondage-play that people describe to me is the teasing element. Sex-play that requires ties, sashes, ropes, handcuffs and blindfolds, etc. means you're constantly building anticipation. Bondage-play also has a number of erotic elements concerning fantasy and role-play. You might have had bondage fantasies and would simply like to experiment a little in your foreplay. That's the beauty of foreplay like this, because you don't have to take it all the way – you can simply tease and tantalise each other a little bit.

Even using just one element, like a blindfold, in your foreplay, you can bring each other to greater heights of desire. Or you might simply introduce handcuffs to add extra spice. The important thing is that neither of you feels threatened that it's going to be some completely perverted and degrading sex session – far from it! Introduce things slowly to each other to experiment with.

The Sex Doctor's Prescription For Feeling Fabulous

Using some of those fun furry handcuffs, lie back and allow yourself to be handcuffed. The agreement is that your lover gets to tease you a little while you're restrained in this way. They can use any of the touching techniques described in the previous chapter.

The Freedom of Bondage

Apart from the extremely erotic visual impact that bondage-play will give you and your lover, many people say it allows them personal freedom to experiment with different roles. For example, you might feel that you have quite a submissive personality type but you'd like to let yourself go and play a more dominant role in foreplay. Or vice versa. Bondage-play allows you to cross between these roles. This emotional freedom also allows you more scope to enjoy fabulous foreplay.

Also, don't feel threatened that somehow you're crossing over into sadomasochistic (S&M) practices by enjoying a little bit of bondage-play. There are differences between S&M and B&D (bondage and domination). Whereas bondage-play involves restraint, control, developing sexual tension, teasing and sometimes using verbal commands to get a lover to 'submit' to your demands, S&M is more likely to involve real pain and degradation. But this is very individual and different people will have their own boundaries and definitions of what they will and will not do, regardless of what they call it.

To get started with a little bondage-play it's important to have good communication with your lover – particularly if they're a new lover. In Chapter 8, on seducing the sexual sense of hearing, I discuss various communication tips. Refer to these tips for ways to communicate sensually.

When Your Foreplay Becomes Bondage-Play

As well as the communication tips you'll pick up in Chapter 8 there are a number of ground rules to ensure your bondage-play is erotic, safe and fabulous. Here are helpful hints to ensure you don't go wrong:

★ Have a code word! Agree a neutral word that tells the other you want to stop what you're doing. It needs to be neutral as we say so many things when sexually excited, and you don't want this word to get confused with something you're crying out in ecstasy.

★ Don't pressure a lover to do something that they find frightening or a turn-off. Likewise, don't bow to pressure from your lover. No one should engage in foreplay or sex that makes them feel uncomfortable.

★ Don't attempt dangerous things! Many people are interested in the idea of autoasphyxiation, in which they restrict their airways or their lover's airways. I have a simple message – don't restrict airways!

★ If you've been drinking or taking recreational drugs, don't get involved in bondage-play. I don't want to sound like a killjoy but drugs and alcohol do change your pain threshold. And you may completely loose your inhibitions and then regret it later.

★ Don't leave your lover alone if you've restrained them in any way. It's not funny and it's not a joke as accidents can happen.

★ If you tie a knot then know how to untie it! You might think this is obvious but people have got themselves quite literally tied in knots that they can't get out of.

★ If a bondage technique feels uncomfortable from the start it's only going to get worse. Let your lover know if something is unpleasant as it'll only become more uncomfortable later.

★ Avoid restraining or tying up any area for too long, particularly when using things like cock rings, which should never be left on a man for more than 20 minutes.

★ Don't forget personal hygiene. When you're both aroused and your foreplay is getting increasingly fabulous, don't get carried away by using a sex toy on, for instance, the perineum or anal area and then moving it up to your partner's vagina.

Restraining Your Lover During Fabulous Foreplay

There are all sorts of restraints available to play with. You'll have plenty to choose from if you visit the Internet sites listed at the back of this book. It's safer to use restraints that are made for the purpose – they usually have Velcro or snaps so you can't get into difficulty with knots. However, something like a dressing gown sash in a nice soft fabric, when tied in a bow, works well and isn't likely to slip into a knot. Restraining your lover creates a wonderful visual image that's a huge turn-on for most people. Here are a few restraint ideas:

★ Your lover's hands can be tied separately (say, to the posts of a bed) or together. If you have a big comfortable chair, let the person being restrained sit in it and tie them to the legs of the chair.

★ Or you can bind their wrists together, either behind them or in front of them. Keep asking what's comfortable, particularly if their hands are tied behind them.

★ You can tie your lover's elbows together. This restraint gives a very erotic image for a man as he can see his partner's breasts thrust out.

★ When it comes to the legs, you can tie the ankles, knees or even the upper thighs together. And when tying a woman's knees together, a man can get a nice tight squeeze if he penetrates her from behind. Experiment with different sensations for fabulous foreplay!

★ When tying the ankles or knees together, remember they can be extremely ticklish – which won't feel very sexy.

★ For an extremely erotic visual display, your lover could sit nude, or in skimpy underwear, at a kitchen chair. Tie their ankles and hands to the chair back and legs, and they're pretty much on display for you. Or have them lie back over a comfy chair and tie their ankles to the legs of the chair for a spread-eagle type exposure.

Other Fabulous Ways to Stimulate the Sexual Sense of Sight

Here are some other suggestions to enjoy during foreplay to stimulate and seduce your lover.

Get Rude With Food

As I'm going to talk about fabulous foods and their place in seduction in the next chapter, on the sexual sense of taste, I'd simply like to highlight here how delicious and tempting food can look.

The lustre of fresh fruits is incredibly seductive. Think of the luscious red hues of strawberries or the deep, rich shades of plums and grapes. There's the sensationally seductive look of figs that have been cut in half and laid on a platter. Or the brighter, lighter hues of melon slices. A platter of rich and ripe fruit ready to be hand-fed to a lover looks fabulous. Watch the way the delicious juices gush from the fruit as you and your lover take a bite.

Then let's not forget the golden colour of melted butter dripping from a delicious asparagus spear. Or the vibrant shades of seafood fresh from the ocean with promises of aphrodisiac qualities.

There are the velvety shades of chocolate and rich desserts. Enjoy the lush cream or chocolate fillings that ooze from éclairs, cakes and pastries. Spoon-feed a rich chocolate mousse into your lover's mouth, or savour the tingling sensation of luscious ice creams as you lick them off a spoon.

Erotica and Pornography

People have widely varying feelings about watching pornography or erotica and/or reading pornographic or erotic magazines. Personally, I feel each to their own, although I am against the stronger sadomasochistic pornography available – but that's just my personal opinion. What counts in using porn and erotica as part of foreplay is how you and your lover feel.

Although men are incredibly visual creatures, it's a common fallacy that women don't get turned on by pornography. As with any potential erotic experience, tastes vary widely. Some porn will turn some women on and turn others off. However, research shows that many women *do* get sexually aroused when watching pornography that they find exciting.

That said, it's how you approach introducing porn or erotica into your foreplay that will help to make it a success or a failure. Here are some key tips:

★ Talk about it first – don't simply whip on a porn film when seducing your lover.

★ Once you've opened up the conversation, you can explore what sort of things they may or may not have seen and what they've liked or disliked in the past.

★ If you both agree you'd like to watch some porn or look through some erotica together, then shop for it as a couple so both of your tastes are satisfied. (At the back of this book there's a list of various websites selling porn.)

★ Don't get into the habit of watching porn or reading erotica every time you seduce each other because people can become porn-dependent.

★ If watching what you've bought disturbs one or the other of you, then stop watching it.

Simple Erotic Pleasures

There are so many simple erotic pleasures (SEPs) that can stimulate you and your lover's sense of sight. Here are a few to experiment with.

Paint Their Fingers and Toes

You can make your lover's fingers and toes look beautiful by giving them a manicure or pedicure. This can be an incredibly sensual and pleasurable experience as the delicate skin of the fingers and toes is packed with sensory receptors. Not only is it an intimate pleasure to perform but the results look fantastic. It will help you bond with each other and can heighten your lover's pleasure.

★ Soak your lover's fingers or toes in warm, sudsy water for a few minutes – use aromatherapy bubble bath for the suds.

★ Gently towel-dry with a soft, warm towel.

★ Take each finger or toe one at a time and gently paint with a gorgeous coloured nail varnish.

★ Treat your lover like a princess, making sure she's warm and comfortable as her nails are allowed to dry. Women can even paint *his* nails for a bit of gender-bending fun – it looks fantastic!

★ Once their nails are dry, watch as they run their beautifully coloured nails over your skin. It's very stimulating to *your* sense of sight.

For Your Eyes Only

There are lots of things you can do in front of a lover that are both incredibly visual and extremely sexually exciting. I'm frequently told, particularly by men, that they would like to watch their girlfriend or wife masturbate. The whole idea of watching her touch herself and get lost in her own pleasure is a huge turn-on. The other thing men frequently raise as something they wish their partner would do is a striptease or pole dance. Of course, men can strip or masturbate for their partner too.

Mutual Masturbation

During foreplay you can use mutual masturbation as a way of learning about your partner's likes and dislikes. Or you can take turns watching each other. After touching and caressing each other, you could suggest that you'd like to watch your lover touch themself.

Turn the lights down low and make sure you're both warm and comfortable. If you feel a bit shy you can leave some clothing on and stroke yourself through it, or for a real tease simply push aside your knickers and touch and caress yourself while partly on view. This was one thing that Victorian prostitutes allowed men to watch, and some men would even get aroused by watching the women stroke their ankles – how shocking in the Victorian era!

It might make you feel more confident to masturbate together. You don't have to go all the way to climax but instead simply touch, fondle, caress and massage yourself so the other can see the pressure and style of touch and friction you use on your own body.

If you're feeling more daring, then demonstrate to them how much pleasure you get from a sex toy. There are lots of suggestions for playing with sex toys in Chapter 8, on arousing the sexual sense of hearing.

Stripping and Pole Dancing

Add movement to touching yourself and you've got stripping and pole dancing. Strip clubs and pole dancing have become incredibly popular – which isn't a good thing for some men who can get reliant on strip clubs for excitement. However, most men and couples can keep this in perspective, with couples increasingly going together to such venues for an erotic evening out. Not only do they both enjoy watching a strip or pole dance, but they get ideas to take back home with them.

To give yourself some stripping confidence, try the following suggestions, and this goes for men, too – let's not forget the film *The Full Monty*!

★ Choose an outfit you really feel sexy and confident in.

★ It's easier to strip off if you choose clothes with zips and snaps rather than anything tricky to get in and out of.

★ Put on some mood music that you enjoy. Some might like a hard rock beat while others might enjoy a little slow R&B.

★ Have fun and start to move in different ways. Experiment with what you think feels sexy. Practice makes perfect, after all.

★ You can try using subtle lighting if you're putting on a show for your lover.

★ If it all goes wrong – you trip or get the giggles – then laugh with your lover! At least you'll have had fun trying something new.

For a little added pleasure and a fabulous addition to your foreplay, you could tie your lover to a chair or the bed and really tease them with a strip or pole dance. The deal is they can look but they can't touch. Flaunt your breasts in their face, rub your hips across their body, and bend over just out of reaching distance. This is bound to drive them completely crazy.

A Pleasure-cise to Heighten the Sense of Sight

Lie quietly in a darkened room with your eyes closed. Allow yourself to imagine the last erotic image you can recall. Maybe you were watching a film recently and there was a passionate scene between two of the actors that you found exciting. Or perhaps you've just returned from holiday and can easily recollect how your new girlfriend or boyfriend looked super-sexy lying on the beach under the sun. Or you caught a glimpse of your long-term partner slipping into the shower that very morning and you thought how fantastic they looked. Whatever the image is, see it in your mind's eye. Developing this ability to recall images while your eyes are closed helps to enhance the sensitivity of your sense of sight.

I hope this chapter has illustrated the amazing power of sight to arouse and awaken desire and lust. From the very first impression a potential lover makes on you, right through to when you're in the middle of foreplay, hand-feeding each other lush, ripe fruit – or from a sensual striptease to the dramatic impact of fetish gear – the sexual sense of sight has a big part to play in seduction and fabulous foreplay.

Let's now turn our attention to the sexual sense of taste.

6. Seduce the Sexual Sense of Taste

The sense of taste is often the most neglected when it comes to sensuality and sexual enjoyment. This is frankly quite ridiculous because taste enters into and has a great impact on our enjoyment of before-play, fore-play and seduction.

Not only does the sense of taste play an essential part in our appetite, but our mouths are amazing pleasure zones. As well as being packed with around 10,000 taste buds, they contain numerous nerve endings. And taste buds are located not only on the tongue and inside the mouth but there are also some on the lips. This is important when we come to fabulous kissing techniques for you to try, later in this chapter.

Taste is important from the very first moment we suckle as an infant, from helping detect what we need in our diet (as when we crave salt), through to the enjoyment we get as our taste buds mature beyond adolescence. A good example of this is the way many young people dislike rich bitter chocolate but later go through a transitional phase where milk chocolate no longer appeals to them, but the subtlety and depth of taste of dark chocolate does.

Rude Foods to Feast on

Before we journey into the wonderful and sensuous areas of kissing and oral sex, let's take a little look at the tastes you can savour with a lover. There are many glorious things to taste and also tempt your lover with. Of course, you need to bear in mind that everyone has their own preferences when it comes to taste.

Many of the 'rude foods' that you can enjoy are also said to have aphrodisiac qualities. Before I provide you with a sensual selection of these to enjoy during foreplay, here are a few 'supper time' seduction tips:

★ Whether you're eating in your kitchen, dining area or in a 'lust nest' you've created, use a dimmer switch or candles for subtle lighting. Not only does this create a seductive ambience, but when you slightly play down one sense (here, the sense of sight with darker lighting), then you automatically heighten other senses – in this case the sense of taste.

★ If you're with someone new you can always practise eating sensually in front of a mirror. Believe me, many people are hung up about the way they eat! And usually for no reason.

★ Have lovely soft napkins and finger bowls ready. It's fun to finger-feed each other but over the course of an entire rude-food feast you may want to clean up your fingertips.

✱ For added intimacy, share one platter of food rather than having two separate dinner plates.

✱ Likewise, if you're mixing up a delectable cocktail, place it in one large cocktail glass with two straws to sip from.

✱ Don't forget the music – as the saying goes, 'music is the food of love' but food is the 'hors d'oeuvres of foreplay'. Slipping morsels of food sensually into each other's mouth is the first course of many!

Rude Foods With Aphrodisiac Qualities

Bear in mind that for many of the following foods you'd have to eat them regularly for them to have an aphrodisiac effect. Generally speaking, most have an overall energising effect rather than a specifically sexual effect. Some of their properties are aesthetically pleasing and may simply seduce you through the senses of sight and taste. That's not a bad thing in itself!

Almonds – The great temptress Cleopatra was said to drink a concoction of ground almonds, spices, honey and yoghurt, which she believed energised lovemaking. Almonds contain magnesium, calcium and vitamin B complex, which supposedly play a role in desire.

Asparagus – You and your lover can hand-feed each other asparagus spears dripping with melted butter – without a doubt a sensual experience. Asparagus is rich in vitamin E – good for your health and libido.

Avocado – Avocados thrive in the climate of South America and the Aztecs called the avocado tree the 'tree with testicles'. They have an extremely sensual texture, being smooth and creamy. They are also packed with essential fatty acids, vitamin B complex and antioxidants, which evidently aid the production of sex hormones.

Bananas – For the most potent result, bake bananas in their skins as this releases an alkaloid in their skin which has an aphrodisiac effect. Many people love their creamy texture and rich taste. Bananas also contain potassium, which has energy-giving properties.

Chocolate – No one can dispute the aphrodisiac qualities that chocolate contains, being rich in energising chemicals – and the darker the better. It also contains phenyl ethylamine, which can give a euphoric effect, as well as energy-giving caffeine and sugar. The ancient Mexican Emperor Montezuma drank 50 cups of pure chocolate every day to fuel the energy he needed to seduce his 600-strong harem.

Figs – The ancient Greeks indulged in orgies once the fig harvest was in. They are not only packed with vitamins, but when sliced in half, the ripe, pink flesh is suggestive of the vagina.

Ginger and ginseng powder – These have been used by the Chinese as a stimulant for more than 3,000 years. Ginger root is a versatile aphrodisiac that can be used in many recipes, and the powders can easily be used in foods such as salad dressings.

Oysters and other seafood – As well as being seductive in the way it looks and tastes, seafood contains high levels of zinc, which benefits healthy sperm production and energy levels. Research also shows that seafood contains two chemicals – NMDA (N-methyl-D-aspartic acid) and D-aspartic acid – that help release both testosterone and oestrogen.

Pumpkin, sunflower and sesame seeds – These seeds are packed with zinc and are beneficial for prostate health and testosterone production in men. Now they are believed to be beneficial for women too.

Strawberries, blackberries, blueberries, raspberries and pomegranates – All of these fruits and berries are packed full of vitamin C, which revitalises sex drive and strengthens reproductive organs.

Many other foods promote increased energy, better circulation and a stronger libido. They include: mangoes, papayas, oily fish, liver, anything from the onion family, sweet potatoes, yams, squashes, spinach, wheat grass, kelp and other seaweed, and yeast extract.

There's been a centuries-old search for the ultimate aphrodisiac with which you can seduce your lover's sense of taste and also entice them through the gorgeous way the food looks. The path has been littered with all sorts of false claims. All of the above foods are good for your health, and many look sexy or certainly can be mixed in with other foods that you and your lover find appealing.

The Sex Doctor's Prescription For Feeling Fabulous

When kissing your lover intimately, pause and place a square of chocolate in your mouth and gently warm it. Then slip it onto her pubic bone to continue melting it – swirling it round and round with your fingers. Then you can finish by licking it off her and your fingers!

More Yummy, Scrummy Rude Foods

The following goodies aren't necessarily aphrodisiacs but are fun and delicious to use in your fabulous foreplay.

★ Anything creamy, such as ice cream, your favourite fruit- or sweet-flavoured yoghurts, or éclairs, mousses, petits fours and cream cakes.

★ Anything sticky, including honey, chocolate, marshmallows, toffee sauces and jams.

★ Anything you can hold with your fingers – which could include mini cocktail sausages, *hors d'oeuvres*, olives (but mind the stones), smoked salmon and other finger sandwiches, and sticky oriental mini-ribs.

★ Finger-sized crudités dipped in luscious dips. Also, try fruits such as grapes, and mango, papaya, apple and peach slices, perhaps dipped in cream or natural yoghurt.

★ Many types of Japanese food are fantastic for hand-feeding, and much of it doesn't use raw fish if this is something you dislike – for instance, vegetable sushi, chicken teriyaki (on skewers) and bean paste sweets.

★ Even chips can be seductive if finger-fed delicately to your lover's lips!

How to Hand-Feed Your Lover Gracefully

You'll not only stimulate your lover's sense of taste by hand-feeding them, but they'll also feel deliciously spoilt. If you're nervous with a new lover, or have never indulged a long-term partner with a rude-food feast, the following tips will help make the experience a seductive one:

★ Wherever possible use small, bite-size pieces. Break items like a delicious slice of cake into small pieces to hand-feed.

★ When spoon-feeding your lover with, say, ice cream, use a teaspoon and not a big dessert spoon – they may feel self-conscious having to open their mouth wide while you angle in a large spoon!

★ Even if using a teaspoon or a small fork, keep the morsels of food small.

★ Try running the edge of the food (where appropriate) around your lover's lips before placing it in their mouth – a perfect technique for a juicy asparagus spear, for example.

★ Have a lovely soft napkin ready to dab the corner of your lover's mouth.

★ Don't be afraid to kiss, with your own lips, any crumbs off their lips.

★ If you're using foods you've heated up, as with a chocolate fondue set, then test the warm chocolate on the inside of your wrist before placing something (a marshmallow or strawberry, say) dipped in the chocolate into their mouth.

★ Don't be afraid to get a little messy with your rude-food feast!

Once you've dabbled in a little foreplay pleasure with food, why not stretch out and become your lover's dessert? Lying where you're warm and comfortable on a big soft towel (for easy washing!), allow them to scatter a few cake crumbs over you or smear something smooth and creamy onto you. They can then gently use their lips and tongue to kiss and lick these little morsels off you.

The Sex Doctor's Prescription For Feeling Fabulous

Grab his attention when eating something that you can handle with your fingers, like asparagus, and linger with your lips gently sucking the tip of it. He'll get the message!

Prepare Your Lips, Tongue and Mouth

When it comes to the sense of taste, kissing is a crucial part of enjoying taste and sensuality combined together. You might think 'a kiss is just a kiss', but believe me, many people lack finesse when it comes to kissing. Some of my suggestions might seem completely obvious but having spoken to thousands of people over the years in my various roles, many people aren't as clued-up as you'd think. Please bear with me if some of these tips for ensuring some seductive snogging seem very basic – even you might learn a thing or two!

★ First make sure your teeth are clean and your breath is fresh.

★ Use non-alcohol based mouthwashes as alcohol based ones dehydrate the mouth, leaving it prone to bad breath.

★ If you're sharing a meal and your partner doesn't want spicy or garlicky food, then avoid it yourself.

★ In your handbag keep some fresh-breath mints or the disposable 'finger sheaths' impregnated with a toothpaste flavour.

★ Never lunge when beginning to kiss; instead start slowly and confidently.

★ As one survey found that 56 per cent of people think men should initiate kissing, then maybe you should begin the kiss if you're a man – or give him the signals that you want be kissed if you're a woman. That said, if you're both attracted to each other, I definitely think a woman should go for it too and begin the kiss.

★ Beware of a soggy kiss with too much saliva! Yes, a kiss should have a certain amount of wetness and certainly as things heat up they may become wetter. But never initiate a kiss with a big slobbering tongue and lips!

★ It's important to loosen and relax your lips so they don't feel hard to the touch.

★ A lengthy kiss is erotic, but sadly this is one of the first things to go out the window when two people become an established couple. So keep the kiss going if you're both enjoying it.

★ There's absolutely nothing wrong with pausing if your mouth or lips get tired. You can stop the kiss and nuzzle your lover's neck or ears before resuming it.

★ You can also use the tips of your fingers to stroke their lips during such a pause.

★ Savour the taste of your lover's mouth and the rest of their erogenous zones, wherever you kiss.

Fabulous Kissing For Foreplay

There are so many fabulous kissing techniques that I have selected only a few of my favourites to describe here. Practically any of these can be used on your lover's lips or anywhere else on their body. Let go and enjoy it – allow your kisses to travel across their lips, down their neck, and beyond. To demonstrate finesse to your lover during foreplay, you can vary the pressure you apply with your lips as well as moving between various types of kisses.

Kisses to Tease and Please With

The Sliding Kiss

This is the beginner's French kiss. Rather than plunging your tongue all the way into their mouth, slide it gently back and forth, or in and out of their mouth. Being gentle and sensual will start to warm up your kissing. It's the perfect kiss to use with the rude-food play discussed above as you can use this tongue action to slide erotic food onto your lover's body.

The Classic French Kiss

No one forgets their first foray into the French kiss. First experiences are usually too wet and tickle too much. The key thing is to relax your lips and open your mouth about halfway. Gently probe the delicate skin inside their mouth with your tongue. As the kiss builds you can also swirl your tongue around theirs.

The Vacuum Kiss

Relax your lips, allowing them to circle around your lover's lips. Apply a soft sucking action that gently pulls on the outer rim of their lips. Pause occasionally and release the pressure around their lips before reapplying. Sometimes it's most successful if you focus on either their upper or lower lip. It's fabulous if you apply the suction to their lip and then alternate this sensation with lightly licking their lips with the tip of your tongue.

The Medieval Necklet

This kiss begins at your lover's earlobe and circles down around their neckline and back up to the other earlobe. Plant gentle kisses as you work your way around this area. You can just imagine a knight of the realm circling the low-cut neckline of a medieval lady with such gentle kisses. For an extra-fabulous tip, use a gentle suction when you reach their earlobe, on the earlobe itself.

The Sloppy Dog

This is the perfect kiss for using on larger erogenous zones like the neck, breasts, abdomen and inner thighs. Allow your mouth to open loosely with your tongue relaxed. Then imagine how you'd 'lap' as a dog would over your lover's erogenous zones. Perfect for lapping up from the base of the breast to the tip of the nipple, where you can gently flick for a fabulous sensation.

The Lush Lap

A more refined kiss than the 'Sloppy Dog', but this one still uses the lapping action. Your lips and tongue need to be more controlled to keep the lapping motion tighter across your lover's skin. Press your tongue reasonably firmly against their erogenous zones and caress that area using a firm lapping action.

The Eastern Swirl and Poke

Since I first described this nearly 10 years ago it has become a very popular kiss. The basis of the kiss is to alternate a swirling action with your tongue with a gentle poking action. You could try this during a French kiss or even along their erogenous zones. As with most kisses, your lips should be relaxed, and alternate the swirl and poke sensations. It's perfect to use on your lover's nipples or clitoris, as long as she enjoys the pressure you apply.

The Mediterranean Flick

It's said that Mediterranean lovers (and perhaps lovers in other hot climates) use this technique for flicking off beads of sweat from a lover's body. A fantastic kiss for when your foreplay is heating up and in the height of passion you can gently flick (with the tip of your tongue) across your lover's lips, cheeks, neck, etc.

The Snake

This is an advanced version of the Mediterranean Flick. Loosen your tongue and allow it to flick, lap, poke and generally imitate the action of the snake's tongue. This can be used during French kissing but also along your lover's body. It's a fabulous technique to use during rude-food play. Try the 'Snake' while moving up and down and around the shaft of his penis or her outer labia during oral sex (there's more about this in the next section, below).

The Stretch

This kiss gives you the opportunity to explore the rarely touched but highly sensitive erogenous zone that's the roof of the mouth. While French kissing, simply stretch your tongue up to the roof of their mouth and gently rub and flick it. This kiss feels potentially explosive since it's such an unusual sensation.

The Sex Doctor's Prescription For Feeling Fabulous

Be creative when it comes to letting your lover know what type of kissing and oral sex feels best for you. A good way to do this is to take their hand and suck their fingers one at a time. As you do this sensually you can tell them that this is the sort of pressure you'd love on your body when they're kissing you.

The Lover's Pass

Another technique to enjoy the sexual sense of taste is to always seize opportunities to turn eating into eroticism. For example, if you're eating something that you can turn into a bit of a rude food, try this – pass it in a sensual way between your lover's lips and into their mouth. Things like a piece of chocolate, fruit or ice are perfect for doing this with. Hold it between your lips and allow yours to touch their lips. Then using your tongue, push the item into their mouth.

Plunging into the Oral Depths

One of the most erotic ways to stimulate your sense of taste is by enjoying oral sex during foreplay. Done well, oral sex feels fabulous! And savouring the taste of their lover is a huge turn-on for some people – whether it's their lover's mouth, perspiration or love juices. But for others that's where the problems begin, as many people are frightened they won't taste very nice, or their lover won't taste very nice, when it comes to giving or receiving oral sex. This is a natural anxiety but one that can be solved. Here are a number of suggestions for getting around this problem.

★ Ensure you're sweet and fresh down below. It's not good enough to have showered or bathed earlier in the day. If you've been on the move during the day and have finally got together with your lover in the evening, you won't still be fresh as a daisy! So take another shower or have a little wash with a face cloth or tissues.

★ Sometimes, though, overwashing with shower gels or douching with vaginal washes creates a less-than-fresh smell for women, as these can upset their normal vaginal PH balance. If you end up with any irritation or an unpleasant smell despite regular bathing or showering, do consult your doctor.

★ Why not have some shower-time fun and take a bath or shower together before foreplay? You can prepare yourselves for wonderful oral sex by sensually soaping each other down.

★ Once out of the shower or bath, taste may still be an issue for some men and women. Give them confidence to indulge in oral sex by smothering the penis or vagina in any favourite tasty treat, like chocolate sauce, fruit yoghurt or honey – or other flavoured things you enjoy. Just beware it's nothing that will hurt the delicate skin of the genitals.

★ If they're still not keen to try oral sex, then encourage them to lick off just a little bit of the food as a compromise. Or they can savour the taste *around* the genitals rather than directly on the genitals.

★ Also, don't forget that the way the love 'juices' taste is altered by what a person has eaten. Spicy and salty foods are the major culprits in altering the flavour of your natural juices.

Now that issue is sorted out – you're bathed *and* swathed in yummy tasting things – don't forget to savour your lover's taste!

Other Oral Tips

As this aspect of foreplay has the power to heighten or diminish a lovemaking session, here are some other helpful suggestions to make it a fabulous and erotic experience that stimulates your sense of taste:

★ Keep your pubic hair trimmed. This makes it easier to keep smelling fresh as well as easier for your partner to give you oral pleasure, as they won't be fighting their way through a pubic jungle!

★ Your tongue is a muscle so get it ready with some exercise! Relax your lips, open your mouth, and flutter your tongue around. You can move it in a circular motion and generally loosen it.

★ When giving oral sex you're likely to use your fingers through touching the genitals. You may gently caress her labia as you lick around her clitoris, or you may stroke his penile shaft as you suck gently on his glans (the head of the penis). Therefore, your hands need to be clean and your nails filed.

★ A common complaint is that often a person is asked to give oral sex but doesn't get it in return. This is terribly unfair and quite frankly bad bedroom etiquette! If you want to receive oral sex then you should expect to give it in return.

★ I'll be highlighting in Chapter 8, on the sexual sense of hearing, how to communicate in sensual tones when in the middle of foreplay. But I'll take this opportunity to emphasise that with foreplay involving oral sex, you need to feel free to discuss your feelings about it. Doing so can remove any anxieties you have and help you understand the way your lover feels about it.

★ With a practice like oral sex it is terribly important to get feedback as you go. Feel free to try some different techniques but keep asking whether it feels good or not.

★ Everyone's different when it comes to where oral sex ends. Many lovers are happy to bring their partner to the point of climax but don't want, say, a man to ejaculate into their mouth or a woman to come in their mouth. That key word 'communication' comes into play again here – you can subtly let your lover know where you draw the line with oral sex through clear communication.

★ A very sexy technique is to use extra saliva from your mouth to lubricate her vagina or his penis. But only if you know each other's sexual history. If both of you are clear of sexually transmitted infections you can safely enjoy the exchange of body fluids.

★ Use a little dirty talk and tell your lover how good their 'love juices' taste.

★ Get really earthy, if you're a man giving her oral sex, by gently sucking out some of her own love juices, swirling them in your mouth with some of your saliva, then feeding it drop by drop back into her mouth.

The Sex Doctor's Prescription For Feeling Fabulous

When giving oral pleasure to a woman it's best to start using your lips only, as her clitoris may be too sensitive to take little licks from the tongue. Begin by kissing her genitals as if you were kissing her lips.

Heighten Your Oral Pleasure

There's oral sex – and then there's fabulous oral sex! You can touch, lick, stroke, flick, kiss and suck your lover all over, to your heart's content. But I'd like to highlight a few special techniques to ensure you both enjoy this amazing part of foreplay – and heighten the pleasure of your sexual sense of taste at the same time.

Loving the Pearl

This technique is best used when she's very aroused. If she likes direct clitoral massage then she'll enjoy this. Rest your thumb and index finger either side of her clitoris. Depending on what she prefers, you can either pull her clitoral 'hood' up or not. Using delicate, little back-and-forth motions, gently stimulate her clitoris between your thumb and index finger. While doing this gently circle her clitoris with your tongue. Build the pace gradually while asking for regular feedback from her on how it feels.

Come on Over

You can stimulate her G-spot at the same time as giving her oral pleasure with this technique. Imagine your index and middle fingers are making a 'come on over here' gesture. Your palm faces upwards. Insert your fingers this way into her vagina. They should reach her G-spot. Use only the index finger if two fingers are too much for her. The G-spot is up a couple of inches inside her vagina on the front (tummy) wall. Apply a gentle stroking motion against the G-spot region as you pleasure her clitoris with your lips and tongue for double pleasure.

Pelvic Rub

When giving your lover oral sex, try stimulating her pelvic region further. With your fingers together, rub gently with circular motions the area a few inches below her belly button. This stimulates the outer reaches of her clitoral 'arms' by pulling on the flesh of the pubic bone while you give her oral sex. Ultimate pleasure!

The Juicer

She holds the base of his shaft with one hand while the other is placed gently on his glans or upper shaft. Imagine that she's about to 'juice an orange'. She carefully rotates one hand back and forth and then starts rotating the other hand too. Keep asking him for feedback as speed is built up and pressure intensified. Now she gently places her lips on the end of his glans and can either suck carefully or lick sensuously as her hands move.

The Double Header

This is another technique that will feel fabulous to him. She wraps her left thumb and index finger around the base of his shaft and her right thumb and index finger above them. As she sucks, licks and flutters her tongue over his glans, she can begin moving her fingers up and down together. Then she gently separates her hands with her left staying at the base and her right moving up the shaft. She very gently rotates them round and round – and then eases her pairs of fingers up and down towards each other and back away from each other.

Pearl Pleasure

Using a pearl necklace (not a real one, mind you!), lubricate the shaft of his penis and wrap the necklace gently around it. With both hands, she clasps his shaft and gently wiggles the pearls and lubricant around the shaft as she sucks his glans.

Never Forget the Golden Rule

Finally, no one should feel pressured into giving or receiving oral sex if it turns them off. To keep things fair, though, if your lover has asked you to give them oral sex and you don't want to, at least sprinkle a few kisses around their genitals while you touch them.

The Sex Doctor's Prescription For Feeling Fabulous

Slowly suck a mint so that your entire mouth is minty fresh before licking the end of his penis or licking her vagina. Your lover will enjoy the tingly freshness of your mouth!

A Simple Erotic Pleasure (SEP)

As we're focused on stimulating your sense of taste, this is the perfect time to try something like brushing your partner's teeth for them. Begin with the front teeth and use small, circular motions on each tooth. Treat each of them as if they're a precious pearl. The gentle technique you apply will make your lover's gums tingle and even if you simply do the front few it's a lovely intimate thing to do together.

Oral Care Fit For Foreplay

To ensure your sense of taste is in tip-top condition, here are the recommendations for good oral hygiene from the renowned American Dental Association:

★ Teeth should be brushed twice daily with an established brand of fluoride toothpaste.

★ Toothbrushes should be replaced every three to four months, or sooner if the bristles look frayed.

★ Clean between your teeth daily with floss or an

interdental cleaner. This is necessary because some decay-causing bacteria (which can result in bad breath) lie between the teeth where toothbrushes can't reach them.

★ Ensure you eat a balanced diet and limit your between-meal snacks.

★ Every six months you should visit your dentist.

★ Ask your dentist about oral care products that might be most effective for you.

A Pleasure-cise to Heighten the Sense of Taste

Taste a flavour that you wouldn't normally try – or think that you wouldn't enjoy. For example, if you don't like sweet things, rinse your mouth with water and then eat a few drops of honey. To heighten the experience, close your eyes and think of your taste buds being stimulated. You might surprise yourself and it'll certainly extend your palate and enhance your sense of taste to do so.

Your taste buds have hopefully sprung to life in this chapter and been stimulated as never before. They play a part in your sensuality and enjoyment of seduction and fabulous foreplay. I'm sure this sexual sense won't be neglected in future! The next sense you're going to develop and refine is your sexual sense of smell.

7. Seduce the Sexual Sense of Smell

The sense of smell is a fascinating and complicated system that affects us far more than we realise. It's one of the two so-called 'chemical senses' because smells are chemicals detected by this sense (taste being the other chemical sense). Through our sense of smell we're continually testing our surroundings. It's a vital part of our life from the moment we as babies begin to recognise our mother's smell, and vice versa.

Not only does smell connect us from infancy to our family, but as adults we are drawn or repelled to people due to their individual smell. This sense is also involved in emotions (it's said we can literally 'smell' fear) and can affect our moods. Sometimes we're influenced at an imperceptible level through smell by the people we meet and their individual scent.

Smell potentially ignites emotions and longings in us even when we don't realise what's happening. Why do you think some supermarkets now discreetly pipe the smell of baking bread into their stores? Because we succumb to the glorious scent and put a loaf in our shopping basket while barely noticing it. Given that we're influenced by many other scents aside from human smells, learning to seduce this sense can enhance your sex life.

Our Scent and Seduction

Research has found that there are many ways human scent has an impact on us. We all recognise the powerful smell of excessive body odour (BO), which most people find extremely unpleasant. But what we don't notice is the sometimes almost imperceptible scent we pick up from another human being which tantalises our subconscious. And in between those two extremes – overpowering BO and subconscious stimulation – we sometimes pick up another person's scent that we're very much aware of but in a pleasant way.

Using this knowledge can help you to successfully seduce someone partly through your own scent – and by recognising that sometimes you may, for instance, be standing close to someone and suddenly feel a little thrill of attraction. You may not be quite sure why you feel this way, but perhaps their scent has prickled your subconscious in a sensual way.

There are some key principles about human scent that you should be aware of, as they are important when considering seduction using the sexual sense of smell:

★ We're very individual when it comes to how much we're attracted to human scent. Some men and women prefer a natural human scent whereas others prefer a 'commercially enhanced' human scent.

★ Believe it or not, perspiration can attract another person! The key is that it's fresh perspiration, which has been shown by research to contain the sorts of pheromones that attract another person.

★ Stale sweat repels people most probably because it means bacteria has started to grow on the perspiration. Because one aspect of our sense of smell is to protect us from danger, we're naturally repelled by the smell of bacteria.

★ Some marketing research has shown that we're very attracted to synthetic smells that mimic pheromones. So if you were to carefully analyse what your nose was picking up in, say, some men's aftershaves, you might be surprised at how very earthy some of the aromas are.

★ Don't underestimate the power of our unique scents. Our primal instinct is to find a partner, seduce them and mate, and this is guided partly by pheromone-type smells.

★ The amount of money spent by perfume and aftershave manufacturers to get their scents just right is phenomenal. But even they can get it wrong. While a woman buys a scent because she likes it, that doesn't mean her male partner will also like it. With this in mind, in terms of attracting your partner, you should probably let them select the scent they find attractive. Because they will choose one that 'speaks' to their subconscious and what it finds attractive.

★ We show exceptional differences in terms of what smells attract us. An ex-lover may have loved one perfume or aftershave you wore but the next lover may be repelled by it. Be prepared to change scents!

★ Your personal scent alters with hormonal changes. For example, a woman gives off a different scent depending on where she is in her monthly cycle.

★ Even if you can't smell yourself, believe me, you give off a scent! No one is scent-free.

The Sex Doctor's Prescription For Feeling Fabulous

To really get you in the mood for foreplay, unbutton your lover's shirt and nuzzle your nose down his chest, around his ribcage and towards his waist. His manly smell will seem fabulous!

Seducing With Your Scent

As I've said, people are very particular about what scent arouses them and what turns them off. You should know this from your personal experience of smells. There are some that you love, some you hate and others you're indifferent to. Bearing this in mind, there's the right balance to be struck between your own natural scent and a commercial scent.

On the Trail of Your Scent

Let's say you're going out for an evening with a new lover or an established partner. It's important to go out fresh and clean but at the same time don't kill off your own personal smell with too much soap, shower gel and perfume or aftershave. This is particularly true now that it's been established that overuse of scented bath gels, soaps, etc, can disrupt the natural PH balance of the genitals and cause an irritation.

★ When you first meet up with your date for the evening, simply give them a 'hello' kiss and let your hair and neckline linger near their face – giving them the chance to pick up your scent.

★ From time to time as you chat, lean in when you're talking and they're listening. They'll naturally be breathing as they listen to you – and will breathe in your scent.

★ As the evening progresses, you might lean over your menu, leaning your head near theirs, so again they can pick up the 'trail' of your scent.

★ At some point, move your hand up to their mouth or chin and gently run your fingers across their chin and lips. They'll catch a whiff of your fragrance from your fingers and wrist.

★ As you walk home together lean your head against theirs so they can smell your pheromones coming off your neck and upper body.

The Sex Doctor's Prescription For Feeling Fabulous

If you're going to be separated from your lover, pack in their suitcase a sweater or shirt you've worn briefly. It will still be clean but it'll contain some of your fresh scent. They can sniff it, sleep with it or wear it to remind them of the lovely you!

Smell and Memory Can Play a Part in Your Seduction

The sense of smell and memory have been shown to be linked. You can use this fact wisely, and in a creative way, in seduction. For example, if the new person in your life tells you an anecdote about how they 'love the scent of pine forests when they go hiking', you can stimulate this good feeling of theirs by using some natural pine scent in your sitting room the next time they come round. Used discreetly it'll simply tantalise their subconscious mind and give them a feel-good sensation. Or you could use it overtly, perhaps burning some pine-scented candles and remarking on their wonderful fragrance.

The Sex Doctor's Prescription For Feeling Fabulous

Bake or cook something that you know appeals to your lover's appetite. It might be a cake or fresh bread, or something else. Instead of cooling it in the kitchen, cool it in the sitting room before they arrive. When they walk in, the scent they associate with pleasure and comfort will subconsciously arouse a positive emotional reaction in them.

Enhance and Increase Desire Through This Underused Sense

Throughout your seduction and foreplay you can do things to reach out to and heighten your lover's sense of smell. I've already discussed kissing, food-play during seduction, oral sex – and many different techniques in previous chapters that can also seduce your sense of smell, including the many touching techniques in Chapter 4. Here are a few extra techniques that'll stimulate the sense of smell.

The Roman Bath

Have your lover sit behind you in a lovely warm bath. Their legs and arms cradle you with your back to them. They reach around you from behind and fondle you with their hands, moving from your breasts and nipples, down your abdomen and down between your legs. While they're touching you encourage them to nuzzle your neck. This'll mean they easily pick up your pheromones as your skin is warm and wet from the bath water.

Torch-light Fantasy

A fun game for couples who are prepared to laugh while they get sexy. While lying in bed with the lights low or simply by candlelight, take turns with a torch to explore under the sheets. The fun part is that the person diving below has to agree to kiss and nuzzle the spots they light with the torch. As your body heat is trapped between the sheets, your smell will be heightened for your lover to pick up. They'll want you even more.

Pearl Necklaces

Women who love a bit of earthy foreplay will certainly enjoy receiving a 'pearl necklace'. A pearl necklace is simply the man ejaculating over her neckline, which often heightens desire because of the powerful scent of their partner's sperm. He may have first received stimulation by his own hand or by her hand. Or she might have been giving him a blow-job, but before he climaxes, he withdraws from her mouth and ejaculates onto her cleavage.

Feminise Him

Many couples enjoy a bit of gender-bending during foreplay. He might find it positively fabulous to be feminised! Extremely masculine men can enjoy it because it releases them temporarily from their traditional role. For others it's just a bit of kinky fun. There are a couple of things during feminisation that will stimulate his sense of smell. Slipping into her sexy lingerie not only feels good to a man prepared to find his feminine side, but also means he can smell her personal scent. Putting on her perfume and lipstick means his sense of smell is stimulated by those cosmetic scents. Remember that even the most outwardly 'macho' men sometimes enjoy a bit of feminisation.

PVC and Leather Fetish

Many people who are into wearing PVC and leather claim that part of the attraction (besides the huge visual appeal for them and the way they feel) is the smell of these materials. Many love the earthy rich aroma of leather or the almost chemical, synthetic smell of PVC. Just wearing one item, such as a PVC corset or a leather mini-skirt, can heighten and tease your lover's sense of smell.

The Sex Doctor's Prescription For Feeling Fabulous

Enjoy some 'fetish play' with your knickers scented with your own love juice! Why do you think internet sites selling worn knickers are so popular? Because the female scent can drive men mad. So send him a pair of your panties for his personal pleasure!

Alfresco Seduction

Many couples enjoy a little sex-play under the stars. Even if most of them keep it to a bit of foreplay rather than going all the way, there's something exciting and a little bit risky about getting intimate outdoors. Whether you choose a beauty spot, a quiet little hideaway when out on a walk, or the sand dunes of the beach, you'll be stimulated in many different ways and one of those will be your sense of smell. The fresh, salty sea breeze, earthy forest smells, floral scents, etc. all go towards enhancing an out-of-door experience.

There are a few things that are key to making an alfresco session really seductive and fabulous. First off, make sure you have a soft blanket if you're going to lie on the ground. Pack something to pull over you to protect your privacy (and not get you into trouble!) or use your ingenuity with, say, a raincoat to cover you. Be aware of things like sand getting into every little nook and cranny. Finally, your lover's comfort is important. It's easy to get carried away by the beauty of a hike in some foothills, press your partner against a tree for some wonderful kissing and forget they might have a branch jabbing in their back!

Turn the Temperature Up

Stimulating a lover with your own intimate scent is certainly an erotic technique to try. For example, be daring when you go out to dinner or for a drink. Pop into the toilet and circle your finger around your genitals – picking up your love-juice smell. Sit back down with them and sensually swish your finger under their nose. Flirt with them and ask them if they love your smell.

Bathing and Showering

You can seduce your partner with many gorgeous-smelling bath preparations. For a truly seductive atmosphere, light your bathroom with sensuously scented candles. Prepare a bath full of sensual, warm bubbles. Mix up some cocktails to sip while you enjoy bathing together.

The Sex Doctor's Prescription For Feeling Fabulous

While enjoying a glass of wine with your lover, refine your sexual sense of smell. Like a wine expert, swirl the wine around in your glass to 'aerate' it, then breathe it in with a long, slow sniff to savour the different 'notes' of the wine.

Other Scents and Seduction

There are many wonderful, unique, exotic or everyday-but-still-delicious scents that you can use to create a whole package of seduction. They can also be used in different ways in your home to stimulate your sense of smell at different points of seduction – from (as noted with a couple of the suggestions above) the point that you and your lover enter your home to when you're finally in bed together.

I'm sure it's now clear to you how important it is to consider what your lover's likes and dislikes are, particularly if you're planning an evening of seduction and foreplay. You'll want to choose a scent that appeals to their tastes. Here I've created for you a list of a number of smells and the feelings they're likely to conjure up in someone.

Heaven-scent

Fruits

Many fruits have wonderful fragrances. There are berry scents – including blackberry, raspberry and strawberry – apple (ripe or crisp and fresh), banana, peach, pear, orange and citrus, pineapple and any other tropical fruits such as mangoes and papayas. Such scents appeal to our carefree and uninhibited side. They evoke images of tropical cocktails enjoyed on holiday with warm sunshine on your shoulders. Think about the last time you had a wonderful fruity cocktail – you might have savoured the smell before sipping it.

Florals

There are so many fabulous floral scents available. From the sweetness of roses and lilacs to the richer scents of lavender and lilies, you can use florals to create an uplifting atmosphere as such scents stir up romance and gentle, sensual feelings. You know what it's like to walk into someone's room where they have a big bouquet of flowers lightly scenting the air – you automatically feel good and fresh.

Culinary scents

There are many fabulous scents available from the kitchen, including those I've already mentioned, such as the smell of fresh baking. There's spicy ginger, chilli and peppers or cinnamon, nutmeg and cardamom – or the fabulous aroma of freshly ground coffee. The scent of a delicious coffee-based drink or dessert speaks to our emotions; after all, we tend to associate cafes with meeting people and socialising. Then there's the savoury smell you get from grilling or roasting Mediterranean vegetables, for example. Some of these culinary smells help to create an exotic atmosphere and others give a comforting feel.

Aromatics

These scents are very much underused when it comes to creating mood and atmosphere. There are many aromatic scents readily available, such as rosemary, bay and thyme. These are fresh and invigorating aromas that can help create a lively atmosphere. They also conjure up images of the sultry and seductive eastern Mediterranean.

Outdoors scents

The powerful smells of the outdoors can be exciting and invigorating. Things like burning wood, pines, sandalwood and other earthy aromas give a deeper sensuality to the atmosphere you're trying to create.

Masculine scents

Musk is a very potent and masculine smell. Sandalwood also has a very masculine smell. These are particularly good scents for people who enjoy a lot of passion. They are found in sprays, candles and pot-pourri, but use sparingly for the best effect.

Creating Heavenly Scents

You can of course create fragrances naturally, through cookery (say, for something spicy or comforting) or by using plants – both florals and fruits placed in bowls or vases will lightly scent a room. But there are all sorts of scents available in many shapes and forms. You can use perfumes and aftershaves dotted selectively around your sitting room, bedroom and bathroom. And you can also buy aromatic candles, lamps, oils, gels and lotions, incense, bubble bath and other toilet preparations, air-fresheners (use natural and environmentally friendly ones) and pot-pourris. Be creative and enjoy the variety of scents available. Using them can create subliminal messages that stimulate sexual arousal and the emotions.

The Sex Doctor's Prescription For Feeling Fabulous

Send your lover a love note but first spray your perfume or aftershave on it. When they open the envelope they'll be reminded of you by the scent.

Scented Lubricants

Lubricant is a fantastic thing! It makes you slip and slide, glide and glisten when massaged into yours and your lover's skin. Only a decade or so ago lubricants had no scent or a rather 'pharmaceutical' type of scent. But now they come with practically any smell you could wish for. Many of the websites listed at the back of this book offer a variety of lubricants.

Don't just use lubricants to brush up on different parts of your lover's body – to feel good and smell good. Use them in fun foreplay too. For example, ask your lover to lie back on the bed and, kneeling above them, squirt a little scented lubricant over your breasts. Ask them to massage it carefully into and around your nipples using lovely circular motions.

Or hold your lover 'captive' by tying them to the bed or chair. Then take their favourite-smelling lubricant and gently massage it into their different erogenous zones. They'll feel increasingly excited with your touch as well as the wonderful smell.

The Sex Doctor's Prescription For Feeling Fabulous

Take your playfulness to more fabulous heights and tie your lover up. Then strip your knickers off and dangle them under his nose as you do a naughty strip. The smell and sight will drive him mad!

Scented or Flavoured Condoms

With all the sexual health scares of the 1980s it became terribly important to encourage people to use condoms, and not only during penetrative sex but also during oral sex. How were women going to be encouraged to give oral sex with a condom on their partner's penis? By giving condoms a scent and flavour! There are many scents and flavours to choose from – from fruit cocktail to chocolate flavoured condoms. Again, you can buy them from many of the websites at the back of this book.

A Pleasure-cise to Heighten the Sense of Smell

It's important to maximise this little-acknowledged sexual sense. Play a guessing game with your lover involving three different aromatherapy oils. Take turns blindfolding each other. The blindfolded one has to guess which aromatherapy oil is being passed under their nose. This forces each of you to identify various scents, heightening your enjoyment of them. For each of the three you get right, you could request a little pleasure from your lover.

I hope you've learnt a great deal from this chapter about an undervalued but important sexual sense. There are so many pleasures to be enjoyed from the sense of smell. Now that you know how it can influence emotions, plus the way your lover experiences things, your seduction techniques can become more sophisticated. There are so many different types of scent to experience to stimulate both you and your lover's sense of smell – remember to enjoy trying new ones from time to time!

8. Seduce the Sexual Sense of Hearing

You might wonder how the sense of hearing has anything to do with seduction, foreplay and sexual pleasure. It's because hearing is an amazing process that allows us to distinguish between something as vastly different as our lover whispering in our ear and that same lover shouting at us when they're angry. It's a sense that's powerful and discriminating, and to fully enjoy seduction, foreplay and sensuality you need to appreciate *every* sense, meaning you can't exclude this one.

Let's imagine an example of how the ear can tune in to what it wants to – and tune out what it doesn't. Let's say that you've just met someone new. You're physically attracted to them but they're boring you with a conversation about their favourite hobby (one which doesn't interest you). Your mind wanders off to what you need to do at work tomorrow. But suddenly they say something about sex – your ear picks it up and immediately you're back in tune with their conversation. Surprise, surprise!

This is important to consider during foreplay and seduction – what will hold your partner's attention and what they'll really listen to. Some research suggests that the human mind tunes in more to vocal tones that are 'emotional' in nature, and also filters in and out key words which have meaning to us. This would imply that your lover is going to listen to you when you whisper to them seductively more than when you speak to them in, say, a nervous monotone. A perfect example of this is Marilyn Monroe's iconic delivery of the song 'Happy Birthday' to JFK. Her breathy, sensual tones will stick permanently in your memory after seeing newsreel footage of that moment.

Our sense of hearing comes into play in many ways. Stimulated in the right way, it can make us feel good. But stimulated in the wrong way, it can make us feel bad or make us want to switch off. For example, excessive noise in your office is tiring and irritating whereas a quiet background hum can be quite calming. As with every sense, people react differently and this is even truer when it comes to sexual arousal and your senses. What seduces one person will turn another off!

Sexual Communication

Let's begin at the heart of the matter when it comes to the sense of hearing – how you and your lover communicate with each other and also the subtleties of that communication. Communication is at the core of the sexual sense of hearing – as well as being crucial to enjoying fabulous foreplay. The increasing popularity of radio demonstrates the importance of the human voice and how it reaches out and communicates with us. Think about it – when you listen to the radio all you hear is the voice speaking to you, or the music playing to you. Nothing more, nothing less, and yet most of us enjoy listening to the radio (despite there being no visual stimulation) and many of us love the radio even more than television.

So what this tells us is that the human voice (and music) can move you, change you, and bring you to all sorts of emotional levels. How can you use this in seduction and foreplay? In all sorts of ways. The important place to begin is learning how to communicate in a seductive and sensual way.

Talking to Your Lover Can Seem Daunting

Once you've got past the initial hurdles that I discussed in the first couple of chapters – meeting and attracting someone – verbal communication becomes even more important. But often the more we see someone, the less likely we are to discuss important issues when they relate to sex. This paradox is due to the fact that the more we like someone, and the more we desire them sexually, the more anxious we feel about not rocking the boat or saying something that they might misinterpret.

We've all been there – put our foot in it in some way, and regretted what we said to a lover. Even if we didn't mean to, we might have hurt their feelings, turned them off, got a reaction we didn't expect, etc. If only from the start we were able to develop our ability to communicate rather than shying away from things. This is particularly true when it comes to bedroom matters. Many people have told me in confidence the sort of things they haven't talked about with the person whom they should be talking about it with – their lover! Here's my advice for stimulating your lover's sense of hearing by speaking to them in a way that'll help you seduce them and enjoy lots of pleasure.

Get the Talking Started

You now know the importance of body language in seduction, but how do you start talking about your needs and finding out about your lover's needs while seducing them? How can you talk to them in a way they'll understand and which might even heighten your's and their pleasure? Begin by talking without speaking!

How to Sex-Talk Without 'Speaking'

Every person makes little sex-sounds during foreplay and lovemaking. Some people stifle them because they worry about making embarrassing noises. But these little sex-sounds are fantastic for sensual communication. You can give your lover important signals about what's pleasuring you with sighs, moans and groans.

The point being, when you want them to do more of the things that make you feel good, these little sex-sounds give them the confidence to continue. It's equally important to listen for *their* sex-sounds. You can get to know their unique noises by 'relaxing' your hearing while you're kissing and caressing and allowing their noises to 'flow inwards' to you. Listen and use what you hear.

Seduce Their Sense of Hearing Straightaway

A key point to remember is that right from the first time you enjoy foreplay with someone, you should talk seductively to them. With all the tips, tricks and techniques in this chapter you can let them know what you want in bed and find out what they would like too.

Time to Talk

Having seduced your lover's sense of hearing by using your sex noises in communication, it's time to start using real sex-talk. One reason why people feel anxious about talking about sex (or talking *during* seduction and sex) is because they don't feel that they're very sexy and they think their voice is going to betray that. And even without reading this chapter you'll know how important communication is and how your voice can betray nerves and anxiety. Let's begin with building your communication confidence before you're with your lover. Try these three critical steps:

1. Practice always makes perfect. Take a few moments to lie back and relax and think about that new special person or the partner you share your life with. How can you let them know what feels good? How can you find out what they want you to do to them? Visualise having this conversation with them. Practise what you would say. For example, maybe you find your foreplay doesn't last long enough. You could practise saying, 'I love it when you massage my breasts during foreplay. I love it even more when you tease me by stroking my inner thighs. It would be fantastic if you could do those things for longer.'

2. Always begin on a positive note. If you want more of something, let them know how fabulous that thing feels as in the previous example. By jumping in with, say, 'You don't spend enough

time on me during foreplay!' you're not going to get as far as you might if you were to begin on a positive note, as I've shown you above.

3. Think about your choice of words and what would appeal to your lover. You know them – at least a little if they're someone new – so think about how *they* say things. By reflecting the way they communicate things to you, what you say will make more sense to them. It's not that you shouldn't have your own style of communication – of course you should – but this technique is more about using this trick of communication to get what you want.

The Sex Doctor's Prescription For Feeling Fabulous

Turn asking and telling what you'd like into a bit of sex-play. Lie on your backs together, snuggled up. Close your eyes, and take turns saying one place you'd like to be touched, kissed or licked. By lying back and closing your eyes you'll enhance your sexual sense of hearing. And it's erotic to listen to the words used in describing the place you want stimulated.

When You're With Your Lover

✦ Definitely when in the mood for seduction, but in your general speech too, use low and seductive vocal tones – I can't emphasise this enough. Shrill, high tones are a turn-off.

✦ Even when flirting, keep to the point. You can lose someone's attention when beating around the bush.

✦ Keep checking on what your lover is thinking about what you're saying. For example, pause in mid-flow and ask, 'Do you think so too?'

✦ During sex and foreplay, definitely use those sighs, moans and groans, coupled with saying things. This will arouse your lover's interest in you and your pleasure even more. I've had many people tell me of their frustrations about their 'silent' lovers. The lover who won't even sigh during foreplay and may not even make any noise when they climax. When a lover doesn't make any noise – when you can't hear any indication of what they're experiencing – it makes it very hard to work out whether they're bored, maybe anxious, or deep in the midst of pleasure!

The Sex Doctor's Prescription For Feeling Fabulous

Create a lust and love tape for your partner. Compile all their favourite mood music onto one CD to give them as a present from your heart.

You Can't Read Minds

Remember you're not a mind reader and neither is your lover. We might think we know what's on someone's mind but we can be wrong. It's natural to feel that when you're close to someone, you desire them, maybe you love them, or even if you're just getting to know them, that you can guess how they're feeling and thinking. Yes, we're very good at reading body language but when it comes to the intimacy required in deepening seduction and foreplay, it's better to get it right. And if you're honest, you might sometimes try to read a lover's mind as an excuse not to communicate with them, particularly if there's something you feel a little nervous about.

When your sexual relationship is advancing and you get to things like fantasy-play, it's very hard to guess what someone really fantasises about. For example, just because your new girlfriend is a college lecturer doesn't mean she wants to get out a whip, put on stiletto heels and 'teach you' what to do in bed. She may never fantasise about being the dominating lecturer who seduces a student.

It's probably even more important to keep that talking going when you're in a committed relationship. Once that golden honeymoon feeling wears off, that's when you need to become more creative in pleasing your lover. This is because early in a relationship you often just get by on animal instinct – and passion! If you've already learnt to be honest with them and talk to them throughout your relationship, it's easier to keep doing so as time goes on.

The Sex Doctor's Prescription For Feeling Fabulous

Try a little subtle 'teasing' when talking on the phone. Throw in the occasional 'flirty' word even if you're talking about a serious subject. This appeals to your lover's subconscious mind and will give them a feel-good vibe throughout the conversation.

Sweet-talking Your Lover into Bed

Speaking seductively to your lover is as much about how you tell or ask them things as what the content is. These tips, tricks and techniques will help you through what you might think is a minefield:

★ Never underestimate the power of your voice to turn your lover on, or turn them off!

★ Whatever you're discussing – a pleasure or a problem – don't allow a critical or negative tone to slip into your voice, as it may sound as though you're criticising them even if that's not your intention.

★ Confidence always enhances the atmosphere. If you sound confident when talking, your lover will feel confident in responding to you.

★ Don't gabble excitedly – for example, about some new sex toy you've bought (more on sex toys later in this chapter). That's a complete turn-off. Instead, try steadying your voice so they respond more positively.

★ Timing is important! In the middle of foreplay don't raise something that's been a problem.

★ Choose a location away from where you normally have sex to chat about serious issues. You don't want your bedroom, say, to become associated with difficult conversations.

The Sex Doctor's Prescription For Feeling Fabulous

Thinking positively has been shown to enhance mood and affect behaviour in a positive way. When on your own do a 'Meg Ryan' from the film *When Harry Met Sally*. Moan and groan and pretend you're building to orgasm to exercise your vocal cords and lift your mood!

Think Before You Speak

Many things you might want to discuss your lover may be sensitive about. Here are a few suggestions for negotiating more difficult sex issues:

★ When on your own, try saying aloud to yourself what you'd like to express to your lover. This will give you an idea of the impact of your voice.

★ Always highlight the things that are fabulous in your sex life before saying anything your lover might interpret as being negative. It doesn't take any effort to tell them, for example, how much you love it when they nuzzle between your breasts, before you let them know you find it less pleasurable when they grab your buttocks every time they climax.

★ Substitution can be sexy! Let's say there's something that you don't particularly like your lover doing and you'd prefer it if they stopped. What's better? To ask them to stop something or to give them a more pleasurable substitute? If, for example, you hate the way they suck your nipples (for a woman) or suck your penis (for a man), simply ask them to 'try kissing my nipples/penis gently with your lips – that'll be a lovely new sensation for me!' They'll interpret this as you being creative and not critical.

✮ Even with a supposed 'issue' in the bedroom, there's nothing wrong with trying to lighten up the conversation. Be playful – for instance, recount the time when you tried to lightly slap their bottom but actually hurt them. You can be self-deprecating and apologetic and then let them know that if you ever hurt them in any way, you definitely want to know. They'll undoubtedly tell you they feel the same and want to know when they're not doing something right.

✮ If your lover still acts like a silent film star and won't utter a sound, then come out with it and tell them what a huge turn-on it'd be if they made little sighs and moans – even talked to you – during foreplay.

The Sex Doctor's Prescription For Feeling Fabulous

Get playful with some sexy chat – turn your communication into a bit of a guessing game and ask your lover what you're describing when you say, 'It involves a pot of honey, a kitchen basting brush, and your lips!'

Crank Up the Sexy Communication

We hear so much sexual banter in our everyday lives – in the office (although political correctness is trying to kill that off), on TV, in films, out with friends, etc. If people were honest, by far the majority would admit that they like a little bit of sexy chat or talking dirty. That said, there are definite rules of etiquette when it comes to sexy chat. With your last lover you might have regularly said things like, 'Ride me, baby, like a cowboy!' But you wouldn't say that with a brand new lover. Some rules for randy talk include:

✱ If you're with a new lover, ask them how they feel about talking dirty.

✱ Always begin on a subtle note rather than plunging in with some really XXX-rated words or phrases.

✱ Sprinkle your seductive chat with occasional sexy comments rather than a constant stream of porn-star quips.

✱ If your lover knows you care about them, they won't be frightened off by a little bit of sexy chat – but don't make them feel like a piece of meat. That said, if they want some raunchy talk which makes them feel like a piece of meat, that's their prerogative!

✱ Learn to talk dirty by, once again, practising on your own. Yes, it does make perfect! Familiarise yourself with different words and it'll build up your confidence.

✱ Try giving each other sexy or dirty nicknames. There's something exciting about the secret little pleasure of knowing you two have named each other's private bits, or a particular activity you do together, etc.

★ Even when talking dirty you've got to make sure you don't criticise your partner in any way.

★ Definitely try some phone sex! If you and your lover are apart you can pleasure each other over the phone. Take your time, lie back, describe to each other what you're touching and how you're doing it. Tell them in all sorts of fabulous detail what you wish they were doing to you at that particular moment.

★ Take dirty-talk to the limits if you're doing a bit of bondage-play or are getting into S&M. As long as you're both in agreement about how far you go, you can take it to the extremes. But to keep things balanced, you could agree that at other times when you're having gentler foreplay or sex, that such chat isn't appropriate.

★ If your lover is aroused by bondage-play or S&M, then the way you seduce them with your tone of voice is critical to its success. If they want to be dominated you have to be commanding, insulting or goading with your voice. Get into it as if you were an actor playing a role.

Just Because Your Last Lover Liked Dirty-Talk ...

A final word on talking dirty is that every lover is different, so you need to be flexible in the way you seduce them with your voice. Some lovers will get completely turned on by your sex noises and once you've made it clear what you want and don't want in bed, they don't want much more conversation. Other lovers will want non-stop sex-talk! Understand who you're with and get to know what they like in terms of communication.

The Sex Doctor's Prescription For Feeling Fabulous

Build up your confidence with talking dirty while having fun! You each have to write down a list of naughty words that you'd like your lover to say to you. Then take turns reading through the lists slowly and seductively.

Heighten the Pleasure During Sex Talk

Just because you're pleasuring your lover's sense of hearing through the sound of your voice, and the sensuous things you say to them, doesn't mean you should stop touching them throughout foreplay. Heighten the things you say by combining them with touch. For example, while whispering to your lover, as you touch each other, that you love a gentle stroking sensation on your inner thighs, then at the same time gently touch them there.

Also, you can demonstrate what you want through touch while you speak. For example, if you've described how much you'd love them to touch your nipples, then gently take their finger, slip it between your lips, gently pulsate it and suck it. Then tell them that's the pressure you want to feel on your nipples.

The Last Word on Communication

Don't let communication – or the 'C word' – scare you! Even if you put your foot in it, say the wrong thing, or say something in the wrong way, you can always apologise. Better yet, you can laugh it off and make fun of what you've said. If your lover doesn't have a sense of humour then maybe they should learn to have one.

By being fearful of real communication, we diminish our sex life. We don't reach the possibilities that are there for us and we don't give the pleasure to a lover that we potentially could. Ultimately, the most important thing you can do is tell your lover you're finding something hard to talk about. Whether it's getting more of one thing, less of another, or trying something completely new, if they're worthy of you they'll listen to your anxieties about expressing yourself.

Tantric Techniques to Tempt and Tease This Sense

When people hear the words 'Tantric' and 'sex' in the same sentence they tend to get wary. There are many misunderstandings when it comes to Tantric practices and sex, but for my purposes here I'm not going to go into an in-depth analysis of all things Tantric. However, when talking about seducing the sense of hearing, it is quite useful to highlight a few Tantric techniques that can help develop this sense. In Tantric practices, a more spiritual energy is tapped into, to be at one with your lover and the universe.

Tantric Breathing

To help stimulate your sense of hearing, why not try some co-ordinated Tantric breathing? Lying on your backs side-by-side, with your bodies touching lightly, close your eyes and begin to co-ordinate your breathing. Use your sense of hearing to guide you and eventually through touch you'll start to feel your ribcages moving together.

When breathing 'as one' couples find it emotionally satisfying and they feel bonded at an emotionally intimate level. Not only does this increase subtle communication between the two of you, but it also increases sensuality. From time to time you can seductively whisper that you want to breathe in this Tantric style together.

Tantric Heartbeat

As with Tantric breathing, it can be a wonderful sensation to listen to, feel and co-ordinate the beating of both of your hearts. One of you lies gently on top of the other so your chests and abdomens fully touch. Resting gently together like this, again close your eyes, listen for and feel each other's hearts. Of course, there are great variations in the speed of people's heartbeats, but together focusing on the soft murmur is soothing, sensually satisfying and also emotionally bonding.

The Whole-Body Orgasm

Now you're ready to try the whole-body orgasm that uses Tantric principles. As your foreplay builds and you start penetrative sex I want you to do the opposite of what you'd normally do. To begin with, listen for each other's breathing and start moving together. Once you're in rhythm together you can start the things that you normally wouldn't. First, start to relax your muscles. As we build to climax we tend to tense up. Gently speak to each other during this point, reminding yourselves to relax those muscles. Next, slow down your breathing. Again, this is the opposite of what we normally do – we usually start to quicken our breathing and it becomes shallower as we get near climax. Whisper to each other to slow down the breathing. Finally, it's time to clear your mind, letting go of any thoughts. Instead try to think of nothing as you slow your breathing, relax your muscles, and listen to your lover.

The Million-Dollar Spot

Tantric practitioners say that there's a million-dollar spot located on a man's perineum. This spot is on the outside of where his prostate is located internally. Here's how to find it:

✯ He should be lying on his back with his legs relaxed open.

✯ She needs to listen to his noises carefully and respond to those.

✯ She can lie with her head across his pelvis or crouch in between his legs.

✯ As he relaxes with his eyes closed she gently rubs, teases and massages his perineum with well-lubricated fingers.

✯ The perineum is the area of skin between the base of his testicles and the top of his anal opening. Most men don't get the chance to experience the pleasure of having this spot stimulated.

✯ He should guide her caresses through pleasurable sex-sounds.

✯ She can also use a vibrator there.

✯ Alternatively, try shaving off his pubic hair and she can gently lick this area, pulsating her tongue, trying to find the million-dollar spot.

The Fabulous Hum of Sex Toys

Something guaranteed to enhance your foreplay and stimulate your sense of hearing is using sex toys. Although there are some quieter ones on the market, most of them make a pleasant little hum as they increase your pleasure. In fact, I know people who get quite a kick out of the buzz of a vibrator, sensing the pleasure that goes with that sound.

The Sex Doctor's Prescription For Feeling Fabulous

Tease your lover by lying back and slowly and sensually rubbing a humming vibrator around your erogenous zones – allowing them to watch. If you're shy you can dim the lights because even just hearing what you're doing will turn them on.

By now you know that when introducing any new sex-play to a lover, you need to do so with tact and consideration. Never excitedly toss a big, shiny, pulsating vibrator onto the bed and expect every lover to jump for joy. Some people – both men and women – feel quite threatened by vibrators. For men it can feel as if their masculinity is being threatened, as if they're not 'good enough'. For some women it is quite daunting simply because they feel fairly exposed being stimulated by a sex toy.

Be sensitive and suggest doing a bit of adult shopping together. Have fun and look at the huge range on offer (check out the websites listed at the back of this book). Many sex toys give as much pleasure to men as women. Be creative and experiment. Here are a few tips:

★ It's important to bear in mind hygiene when using sex toys. For example, if you use an anal vibrator it shouldn't then be used on her vagina. Keep separate sex toys for each other.

★ Clean your sex toys as per the manufacturer's recommendations on the box.

★ Before you even contemplate using a new vibrator during seduction and foreplay, get used to the way it works. Some of those mentioned below are a bit complicated.

★ Don't use everyday items as makeshift sex toys! I've a brother who works as a doctor in A&E and he's told me some terrible tales of sex-play gone wrong!

★ As well as pleasuring each other with sex toys, you can of course use them when you're on your own for self-pleasure.

★ When using lubricants, choose water-based ones that won't break down the surface of your plastic-based toys. Some lubricants are made for this purpose, like the Ann Summers Slide and Ride.

★ On the whole, vibrators should not be used on one spot for longer than 20 minutes maximum. You can overstimulate the sensitive skin of the clitoris, the genitals generally, the anus, etc.

A Selection of Toys to Tease and Please Your Lover With

There's a vast array of sex toys out there to satisfy everyone's desire. Here's a selection of some classics and some more unusual ones to try.

Fingertip Vibrators – For delicate, sensual pleasure, try some of the toys that slip onto your finger, such as The Zing Finger or the Fukuoku finger massager. There are many variations that can be slipped onto his or her finger. Perfect for stimulating small areas like the nipples, clitoris and perineum.

The Fukuoku Glove – This gives you five fun-filled vibrating fingers when slipped onto the hand. It's not a cheap toy, mind you.

Clitoral Ticklers – These toys can either be attached to full-sized vibrators or used on their own. They come in different shapes to pleasure you with.

G Art Bullet – A vibrating bullet shape that has different pulsing options.

The Durex Play Charm – Microphone-shaped, with three speeds and a pulsating option, it's great for clitoral and pubic region stimulation.

G-spot Aqua Vibe – This is a great introduction to a G-spot stimulator and it's also waterproof. It has the 'come over here' crooked-finger design with multi-speed settings that vary from subtle to powerful vibrations.

VibraExciter – A sexy mobile-phone accessory that's connected to a bullet vibrator. You can set it to start vibrating when your mobile rings or when you receive a text. Perfect for playing lovers' games!

Vibrating Rock Chick – Stimulating both the G-spot and clitoral region at the same time, this is quite an ingenious vibrator.

The Jessica Rabbit or Pearl Rabbit – This is the classic, rather strange-looking 'Rabbit' that has been tried and tested by huge numbers of women. The main vibrator penetrates the vagina while a small projection also stimulates the clitoris.

Three-way Rabbit – This one hits all the spots with its multiple vibrations that stimulate the clitoris, vagina and also the anal area. As with other Rabbits, it looks unattractive, but does the job.

The Promise Vibrator – A vibrator with a very good shape for G-spot stimulation.

The Hummingbird Triple Pleaser – For those who like anal pleasure, this toy combines anal beads with a vibrating, hummingbird-shaped clitoris stimulator. The wings of the hummingbird vibrate the labia.

Liberté – Looking like a piece of art, this vibrator is designed to hit the G-spot. It can go up to quite powerful vibrations.

Clitoral/Pubis Vibrators – These are excellent for women who like the whole clitoral or pubic region vibrated. They give her a fabulous feeling, perfect for seduction, by ensuring she's ready for full pleasure.

Tongue Vibrators – These are fabulous way to give oral sex sensations to your lover as they clip onto your tongue during oral sex. They really are made for your ultimate pleasure!

B-doyng – This is a 'personalised' vibrator that you have with your own sexy saying or message branded on it. Interesting technology means the tighter you hold on to it, the more the pulses increase.

Vido V8 – This silicone toy made with Vido technology responds to your clenching and will exercise your pelvic floor muscles.

Hi-tech Vibrators – For a more lifelike, very skin-like feel, check out vibrators that are made from Technoskin and UR3 materials.

The Butterfly – This unique device may need some experimentation to get it positioned how she likes it. It straps onto her thighs and has a central, flat vibrating region that is positioned over her genitals.

Harnesses for Him – There are many vibrators that are held in place over his penis and testicles, with attachments for vibrating against her genitals during penetration. Some are flexible and can hold a vibrating 'bullet' or clitoral stimulators of varying designs.

Glow-in-the-Dark – If you don't feel you have a lot of body confidence, why not have fun with a glow-in-the-dark vibrator? Follow the buzzing wherever it goes!

Slightest Touch System – Many women claim to be brought to a pre-orgasmic state by this system. She attaches electric pads to her ankles and the current is sent up to the pubic nerves to stimulate the pelvic region. However, doctors debate the effect and it may be a placebo or simply a soothing effect that these women are experiencing.

The Sex Doctor's Prescription For Feeling Fabulous

Try slipping a vibrator between the two of you while kissing and caressing. This can heighten your foreplay and enjoyment.

Extra Pleasure From a Vibrator

When it comes to the female orgasm, research shows that a woman is more likely to have a second or multiple orgasms if she is stimulated in different ways. Let's say that during foreplay you've brought her to orgasm manually or orally. If you then use her favourite vibrator on her, she's more likely to have a second orgasm. It's important to note that many women don't reach a second or more orgasms, and they shouldn't feel like a failure if they're not multi-orgasmic.

The Sex Doctor's Prescription For Feeling Fabulous

Is he a shy-guy? Many men are curious about what a vibrator would feel like running over their penis, around their testicles and down their perineum. But because they feel sex toys are meant for women, they won't suggest it. So when you've got your toy out, ask if he'd like to experience it! If he wants anal stimulation, use a separate toy or ensure proper hygiene.

Get Ear-otic!

You now have at your fingertips many techniques for sensual communication with your lover. Stimulating their sense of hearing with your vocal tones and the things you say should now be easier to achieve. This is the perfect time to think about fantasy-chat during foreplay.

Delicious Descriptions of Fantasies

Here's how to get started when sharing your fantasies during foreplay. You need to have a level of trust and respect for each other so that you both feel you can be honest about your secret desires.

★ Agree who's going to go first.

★ Lie back, close your eyes if you like, and gently touch each other as you describe your fantasies.

★ Don't laugh at their fantasy. Laughter is great in the bedroom but it should be *with* someone and not *at* them!

★ Use lots of delicious detail in your fantasy descriptions. This is a big turn-on.

★ Remember that you'll stimulate their sense of hearing with seductive vocal tones.

★ Be tactful – your lover should feature in your fantasy. If you drone on about some hot Hollywood star you want to have sex with, it may turn your lover right off. But put them square in the middle of your threesome with that same Hollywood star and they'll probably love it!

Some Fabulous Female Fantasies

Obviously everyone has their own private fantasy world and what turns one person on may turn the next one off. However, there are a number of common fantasies that many women have. Encourage her to be honest about her secret world of sexual thrills. You can kick-start the conversation by asking about particular fantasies. Here are a handful of fantasies you might find she enjoys.

★ Being dominated by a powerful man – whether it's a policeman, a soldier or some unknown stranger, she may find it exciting to fantasise about passionate sex without inhibitions.

★ Being a dominatrix. Many women love the thrill of fantasising about being a professional dominatrix: getting men on their knees, having them beg for mercy, whipping them, etc. This is a 'disinhibiting' or 'freeing' fantasy, particularly for a woman who might be a little inhibited.

★ Lesbian love – many women fantasise about making love to a woman. They wonder what it would be like, what the differences would be, how it would feel, and so on. Such fantasies may or may not have implications for their sexuality.

★ Doing something outrageous and 'dirty'. Again, because many women feel quite inhibited about their bodies, or shy about asking for what they want, they often fantasise about having some sort of outrageous sex.

★ The handyman – being ravished by a ruggedly handsome plumber, electrician, stable lad, etc., in a wanton way is a highly popular fantasy. Having spontaneous and abandoned sex with someone who's just a sex machine, and no more, can be a big turn-on.

It's important to remember that just because someone fantasises about something, they may not necessarily want to act it out!

Some Fabulous Male Fantasies

As with women, the range of male fantasies is vast. Many men's fantasies seem to directly reflect the idea of freeing themselves up from their traditional male roles while others represent their individual quirks. Some common male fantasies include:

★ Group sex or threesomes – although many women fantasise about these, more men do. Men get turned on by the idea of working through a multitude of willing partners at the same time. It boosts their sense of masculinity.

★ Voyeuristic fantasies. This means watching their girlfriend or wife have sex with someone else, and has links with the fantasy above. Many men fantasise that they'd watch their partner being ravished and then take over, proving they were better than the other man.

★ Being dominated by a powerful woman. Whether she's a dominatrix or a strict schoolmistress, being told what to do and how to do it is a big part of many men's fantasies.

★ The naughty nurse – having a sexy and randy nurse take advantage of them when they're helpless in their hospital bed is another common fantasy.

★ Risky sex. Fantasies about things like taking a colleague over the photocopier, in the stationery cupboard, or picking up someone in a bar and having sex with them round the back in an alley are all big turn-ons.

The Sex Doctor's Prescription For Feeling Fabulous

Turn fantasy-play into a little game. One of you agrees to go first. You say the opening line of a fantasy scenario. Your lover says the next line. You then take turns as you work your way through a fantasy. Between both of your imaginations, you'll end up turning each other on with your suggestions!

Get-in-the-Mood Music

The power of music to move us, arouse us, and alter our emotions is well-documented. That's why music therapy is used for all sorts of emotional problems, to help people overcome their problems and enhance their wellbeing. When it comes to music and sensuality, tastes vary tremendously. For example, one woman may be turned on by listening to Robbie Williams sing his famous ballad 'Angels'. It uplifts her, she feels in the mood for romance, and she feels warm and cuddly – and sexy – listening to it. But another woman might cringe when she hears that ballad and might be turned off by it. One man might love listening to the raucous sound of Guns N' Roses, and it might put him in the mood for lustful sex, yet another man might laugh at their stadium-rock sound.

Music to make love by ranges from driving rock to 'mood' music such as R & B. These have different effects on different people. When thinking what to play for your lover, consider both of your tastes and the mood you're trying to establish. But don't underestimate how much what you choose to play may or may not appeal to them.

The Sweet Sound of Humming

One fun technique involving the sense of sound can be tried during oral sex. When you go down on your lover, simply place your lips around one part of their genitals and hum gently. For example, she can hum while she holds one of his testicles or the end of his penis in her mouth. He can hum while gently placing his lips around part of her labia. You can hum a tune or just hum aimlessly, but the vibrations from your humming will feel fabulous.

The Sounds of S&M

I've already mentioned S&M briefly. But I think it's worth noting that when it comes to stimulating the sexual sense of sound, many in the S&M world get off on the sounds of someone being paddled, spanked or whipped. Not only do they like the 'thwack, thwack' of someone's bottom being spanked but they might also enjoy the 'swish' of a riding crop or a whip. People have told me how such sounds turn them on and that these sounds are very much a part of the atmosphere created in this type of sex-play. In particularly, a 'Bottom' (the name for the masochist or person receiving punishment) in S&M-play might wait with bated breath for the sound of, say, the whip swishing down just before striking them. A 'Top' (that is, the person giving the punishment) might be less likely to be turned on by that sound, preferring the sound of the gasp or cry of the 'Bottom' – *that* turns them on!

The Sex Doctor's Prescription For Feeling Fabulous

Leave your lover an answerphone message with a difference. Lower your vocal tone, slow your vocal speed and speak sensually. Keep it brief but make your point – seduction is in store tonight!

Sensory Deprivation to Heighten Your Pleasure

Earlier in *Fabulous Foreplay* I mentioned blindfolds in relation to bondage-play. Having fun with a blindfold can benefit your sexual relationship in many ways. First off, it's good, kinky fun and you can play various sex games with a blindfold. For example, the blindfolded partner has to guess what their lover is touching them with – is their inner thigh being stroked with their lover's tongue, finger, or the end of his penis? But as well as having such fun, you'll find that as soon as you take away your sense of sight, your other senses are heightened and become more sensitive to stimulation.

This is particularly true when it comes to the sexual sense of sound. For some reason we tend to use our ears as our second 'eyes' when we lose our sight. So why not blindfold your lover and try a variety of things to heighten their sensitivity? Put on some music you both like and use techniques such as 'feathering' (as mentioned earlier, drizzling massage oil on their body and running a feather through it), or ice-cube play (putting an ice cube between your lips and running it over their erogenous zones). Your sense of hearing will also get the benefit of their little gasps and shrieks as you do this!

Generally speaking, playing with blindfolds builds more trust in your relationship too. You'll both begin to trust the other more when you allow yourself to be blindfolded and find out that your lover is only going to give you fabulous foreplay and tease you and please you.

A Pleasure-cise to Heighten the Sense of Hearing
The ear is not only the sensitive vessel of hearing, but is also incredibly sensitive itself. Close your eyes, lie back and have your lover gently nuzzle your ear. Enjoy the wonderful shivers that the touch of their nose brings you. Relish the gentle and erotic sounds of their breath.

I've now taken you on a sensual trail through the five classic senses. Each and every one of them can be teased and pleased as part of fabulous foreplay. Now it's time to take a look at your *sixth* sexual sense and how it can enhance your sexual pleasure.

9. Seduce the Sixth Sexual Sense — Intuition

Having explored how you can tease and please your lover through the five classic senses, I'd like you to open your mind to the idea of your sixth sexual sense – your intuition. An idea from the Gestalt school of psychology might help explain this – with their idea, or theory, that when considering the function of an entire, complicated system, the whole is greater than the sum of its parts.

It's an excellent way of looking at the six sexual senses. Each of the individual five classic senses can provide a wealth of information. Understanding and using each sense can heighten your experience of seduction and ensure foreplay is fabulous. But to understand your sixth sexual sense, I'd like you to think of all five of those classic senses coming together and what they give you – as one big, whole package – which is greater than each one individually. That is your sixth sense. Your intuition can be thought of as all of these sensory aspects working together, feeding you information about your lover and their needs and desires, and about your own feelings, arousal and desire at a greater level.

This is particularly true when gauging someone's mood generally, and for specific things such as gauging their reaction to a sexual suggestion of yours. Think back to what I told you about body language and how your mind sifts through lots of signals from someone and comes up with an answer or conclusion. For example, when you see someone across a crowded room and you start to assess all sorts of signs and signals from them, and come to the conclusion that they'd like you to smile at them and chat them up. It's no one sign or signal which gives you that conclusion. It's your assessment of the whole situation, at many levels, and all this can happen extremely quickly.

You can put your sixth sexual sense to good use. But first I'd like to answer a question you might be thinking about, and that's why did our sixth sense evolve in the first place? What good was it for humans? Many people believe that it evolved to guide our most basic instincts of survival and reproduction of the species.

When it came to survival, our ancient ancestors needed to judge (sometimes imperceptible) signals from a situation and make quick decisions about how they should react. We've got to remember that ancient humans were continually encountering new situations that they didn't have experience of. So they needed something to guide them – like their intuition.

It was the same when it came to the importance of reproduction – sex – as ancient men and women obviously needed to ensure the species continued. Long before they developed a sophisticated language like ours they had to 'guess' about things like fertility and who would be a good mate to ensure healthy offspring. As humans we became very good at judging who was receptive to our advances and who would be a good mate for our benefit.

Here are some ways to put this sense to good use when it comes to seducing someone. As with most of my suggestions, the majority of these apply equally to someone new in your life or someone you have a relationship with already.

Try Mind Reading

I realise that when I discussed communication techniques, I asked you *not* to try to be a mind reader – but in order to develop your intuition I'd like you to do a little experimentation. When you two are relaxed and have been enjoying a little foreplay such as touching, kissing and caressing, dim the lights, turn down any music and look into each other's eyes. Try to see the inner person in each other. Relax your mind and clear it of thoughts besides your enjoyment of this intimate moment. Next, take turns trying to guess the other's thoughts. You'll be surprised by the signals you can start to pick up when you're both relaxed and 'into the moment' with each other.

Sounds of Pleasure

You can have some fun with this little technique, but also enjoying the pleasure it gives you will help develop your intuition. You already know to listen to your lover's sex-sounds during seduction, but now I want you to turn this into a sexy little game. In the following, take turns being the one who's being touched.

Your lover lies down where they're comfortable and warm. Warm up your hands by rubbing them together and then, using massage oil, gently start touching your lover. Ask them not to use words but only sex-sounds and their own 'vibe' to let you know what feels good, what feels great, and what feels fabulous. Stroke them, tease them, perhaps use some 'feathering', which I've already described (Chapter 4), to generally determine *with your intuition* what's pleasing them.

You won't even realise how your own subconscious mind is extracting all sorts of little messages from them as you pleasure them. These little messages will guide you to the places that feel fabulous instead of those that feel merely 'good'. I recommend couples doing this every couple of months to re-establish their intuitive knowledge of each other rather than taking each other for granted.

The Gift of Lust or Love

Take this opportunity to select a gift – something that's out of the ordinary but which symbolises your feelings towards your lover. When I say out of the ordinary, that doesn't necessarily mean expensive – far from it! Instead I want you to use your imagination and creativity in choosing something. Once you've chosen it, I want you to give it to them over a romantic dinner and ask them if they can guess what it symbolises. You might choose something artistic that strikes you as symbolising, for example, your passion for your lover or the gentleness you feel from them. Or maybe choose a plant, or an animal-shaped soft toy (but not a cheap and nasty one!), that represents an aspect of your feelings. Perhaps a beautiful seashell will mean something to you. Whatever gift you give, simply use your own intuition about its symbolism to 'tickle' your lover's intuition into action.

Back-to-Back

This little exercise will continue to develop your intuition about your lover's mood. Get comfortable with them and sit back-to-back with as much of your hips, back, and the backs of your heads touching. If you want to, you can reach around and clasp hands or link elbows in this back-to-back position. Without saying anything, try to 'sense' what they're feeling, taking a few moments to absorb this. In a similar way to the Tantric exercises described in Chapter 8, you'll probably find your breathing rate starts moving in time with your lover's. As you both relax and sense each other's mood, it's amazing the sort of intuitive bond you develop.

The Sex Doctor's Prescription For Feeling Fabulous

Agree to make love with your partner without any talking. Instead, the whole experience from foreplay to finish is about listening to the sighs and sounds you both make and developing your intuition about what's feeling right between you.

Boost Your Sexual Confidence and You Boost Your Sixth Sense

Sexual confidence is terribly important to being skilled at teasing and pleasing your lover. Of course, it's bound up with your general confidence too. It's important, on a daily basis, to remind yourself of your fabulous qualities as a lover. Remind yourself of the last time you enjoyed foreplay and seduction. What did you do that made it special for you and your partner? Did they tell you they loved something you did when you were kissing or caressing them? Or did they experience the best-ever climax? Enjoy the delicious detail of these memories and allow them to boost your sexual confidence.

How does this fit in with your sixth sense – your intuition? When you're feeling sexually confident you'll be more in tune with your lover's needs. The self-belief you have will mean you believe in your judgement. This sexual confidence of yours will rub off on them. It's an upwards cycle of confidence, understanding and enhanced intuition.

The Sex Doctor's Prescription For Feeling Fabulous

Get playful with your lover when teasing them. Have them lie on their stomach so you don't have eye contact and caress their buttocks, back and legs with a variety of the touching techniques I've shared with you (Chapter 4). Then reach between their inner thighs and tease them further. They're not allowed to tell you, but instead use your intuition for when you think they can't take any more teasing – and need some pleasing!

More on Self-Belief and Intuition

Don't buy into the myth that just because your friend enjoys something, such as being tied up and teased with a sex toy, you're going to enjoy the same thing. You might not enjoy that at all. Give yourself the right to be your own person with your own desires! Again, this will boost your sexual confidence, increasing your sense of intuition.

Ban Sex to Heighten Intuition and Desire

You may be wondering why on earth I'm advocating a sex ban. Well, this applies to established couples rather than those in the first flush of lust! Banning sex for a limited period is a unique and powerful way to help you reconnect romantically and also to think more creatively about your sexual relationship. It also helps with the problem of taking each other for granted and slipping into bad sex habits. It'll help to develop your intuition and to kick-start your sexual desire.

Not only does a ban rebuild romantic and emotional intimacy but it also allows a couple to act like they're new lovers who are building up to sleeping together. And who are in that delicious phase of mounting sexual tension.

You might want to try a partial ban. For example, you could agree to a ban on making love in your usual place for a month but allow yourselves to work out another place where you might enjoy having sex. You can turn this into a bit of intuitive teasing where you both guess where would be the place your lover would like to seduce you.

Alternatively, you could use a partial ban to apply to the time of day that you usually tend to seduce each other. Agree that you'll use your intuition to 'guess' when the other feels sexy. Even if it doesn't lead to full sex, it's about using that sixth sense to pick up any little signals they're giving you, outside of the time frame when you ordinarily 'know' you're going to have sex.

You can use a sex ban to increase sexual tension when you're out and about together. Watch out for little signs in each other of flirtiness or sexiness. Stroke him under the restaurant table if he gives you a certain look that pricks your intuition. Caress her quickly as she looks into a shop window displaying attractive clothes because you know she loves dressing up – and you're intuition tells you she'd like to be touched.

But please note, you should only agree to a sex ban to heighten your feelings for each other without pressurising each other.

Enhance Your General Awareness

Where do you make love most frequently? Is it in your bedroom? Does it tend to be cuddled up on a big, soft sofa in your sitting room? Or is it somewhere else? I'd like you to go to that place on your own, and relax and simply absorb the atmosphere. I've already described to you how colour and design can affect your mood, in turn affecting foreplay and seduction. Now I'd like to think about the whole atmosphere your intuition picks up. What does this area tell you? How do you feel when there on your own? Get used to absorbing everything around you in the place where you tend to seduce your lover. You may decide to make some changes to that area.

Try a Little Role Swapping

As you get to know a lover more and more, and perhaps your relationship deepens, it's easy to get stuck in the same role that you 'play' with each other. This decreases your sixth sexual sense as you take for granted what you think they'll want or like. Forcing yourself to swap roles will increase your intuition.

Have fun with this, and you might want to plan it in advance. For example, if you're getting together on a Friday night, agree right from the beginning of the evening that you'll be swapping roles. If one of you tends to be the 'initiator' when it comes to sex-play, then the other should do so that evening. Swap around all of the things you normally do. Think outside your sexual 'box' so to speak. You may be surprised by the results of the evening!

The Sex Doctor's Prescription For Feeling Fabulous

Test your developing intuition with a little phone-sex game. Get graphic in your descriptions about how you're touching yourself and with what (eg, a sex toy or your hand). But don't say where you're touching yourself! Then lie back while holding the phone, and as you touch yourself – and get into the pleasure of the moment – they have to guess where you're doing this.

A Pleasure-cise to Heighten this Sense of Intuition

Visualisations are terribly important to building this sixth sexual sense. Get comfortable and lie back and visualise yourself as a sex god or goddess. You look radiant and seductive. Hold this delicious picture in your mind. Put in as much detail as you want – you may have sex 'slaves' pandering to your every need – and bring this image to mind before you next see your lover. You'll radiate your sex god/goddess vibe, making it easy for them to pick up.

I hope you're now thinking about your intuition and how important it is as a sexual sense. It helps you pull together every message, sign and signal your new lover or long-term partner gives out. It also increases your awareness of your surroundings, and it can be developed with your newly raised awareness and by trying out the techniques I've suggested. Hopefully you'll find that your intuition increases right across every area of your life as you open your mind to using it. Finally, it's time to turn to some 'After-play', as I call it.

10. After-play and Afterthoughts

You've now read about all sorts of suggestions to tease and please your lover with during foreplay and seduction. You can arouse every single one of their six sexual senses now that you've got a good understanding of the amazing ways to stimulate them. Or if you simply select and use one or two new techniques every so often, you can improve and enhance your sex-life.

This means you're now perfectly equipped to develop any of these suggestions and techniques into full-blown lovemaking. For example, think about all the touching techniques in Chapter 4. You could caress your lover and bring them to full satisfaction with some of those methods. Or what about the oral sex techniques from Chapter 6? By kissing, licking and sucking your lover where it pleasures them most, you can take them to the peak of enjoyment. And from Chapter 8 you can go to town with some of the sex toys I've mentioned and bring each other to climax. Or use some of those sex toys for extra stimulation during penetration. These, and so many more things, can give you a huge amount of pleasure all the way from the beginnings of seduction, during your foreplay, to your final satisfaction.

But what about 'After-play'? After-play is how you treat your lover once you've had sex – the things you do that give both of you pleasure and make the most of your satisfaction. Yes, it's important to create a sensual and exciting atmosphere when thinking about Before-play, which I highlighted right at the beginning of *Fabulous Foreplay*. And then as you actually begin to seduce your lover, it's important to keep com-municating and learning about what teases and pleases them. But you can't just leave it there and forget about the rest of your intimate life. That begins with After-play.

Developing Your After-play

Here are some key things to ensure that you deepen and enhance your enjoyment of each other. When After-play is successful, you're more likely to have more sex!

Be Sensitive

You may feel like rolling over and falling asleep after you've reached orgasm. That includes some women too, although more men do this. But at the very least, whisper something loving or sensual to your lover before taking a nap.

Be Genuine

Whatever you say to complete the sexual bond you two have just experienced, make sure you genuinely mean it.

There's nothing worse than telling either your new or an established lover that it was the 'best sex you've ever had' when perhaps it wasn't. If they paid attention to the messages about body language and intuition, they'll know immediately that you're not being completely honest. You can genuinely tell them how much pleasure you had, you can highlight what felt the best – just be honest!

Be Gentle

Whether you spend one minute or one hour holding each other and feeling that wonderful après-sex vibe together, make sure you touch the other gently. They may be very sensitive to the touch after orgasm. Run your index finger down your lover's breasts and abdomen. Stroke their hair softly as you move any ruffled hair away from their face. Hold them tenderly. Whisper quietly – their sense of hearing will have been heightened with lovemaking. Keep movements slow, gentle and sensual.

Keep That Teasing Going

If you've had a good time you can be flirty in your After-play chat. You can whisper how much you'd like to do it again; you can tell your lover in really dirty detail exactly what excited you. Be playful with your touching, for example, skimming your fingertips across their favourite erogenous zones, which are already ripe for more pleasure, having had their sensitivity heightened from your lovemaking.

The Sex Doctor's Prescription For Feeling Fabulous

Without directly touching her clitoris or his glans, gently ripple your fingertips near these areas as you go to hug your lover. Between the tenderness of your gesture and the eroticism of your fingertips, they'll feel fabulous.

Seconds Don't Have to Be Sloppy

Once you've rested and relaxed in that post-orgasmic haze, and you've cuddled and snoozed, you may both be in the mood for seconds. Why not give each other a sensual 'sponge bath'. Using warm water and soft facecloths, take turns simply bathing each other. Gently stroke the soft cloth over your lover's genitals. Lavish attention and tender care on them. Or get into a warm shower and caress each other as you wash the previous lovemaking away.

Sometimes Seconds Are Quicker

If you've enjoyed lots of the fabulous foreplay techniques and stimulated many of your lover's sexual senses, then for the second time around you might be a bit quicker. Here are some 'quickie tricks' to help you press each other's buttons.

★ Do either of you have one 'perfect' way of touching the other that turns them on? Definitely let your lover know which technique really does the trick so they can use it to turn you on quickly.

★ Make second-time-around sex different from the full-on sex you've just enjoyed. For example, if you shower after lovemaking then you can bend your lover over the bathroom sink counter for some foreplay and teasing.

★ You should both always know (through good communication) that you might only want a little fooling around that may not lead to full sex. A little bit of extra pleasure doesn't have to go all the way.

Let a Little Laughter In

Let's say something didn't go quite to plan in your lovemaking. There's no need to get upset or stressed about it. Equally, you shouldn't be anxious or worried. It's important to lighten up and even laugh a little together about what you've just experienced. Why is it so important to your sex life to be able to laugh together? Because people take sex far too seriously! Yes, seduction can be erotic, foreplay can be fabulous, and sex can be amazing, but that doesn't mean you should approach it like two scientists trying to work out the best formula. There are times when everyone experiences some sort of difficulty in the bedroom and being able to laugh about these times rather than feeling humiliated or embarrassed is by far the best approach.

After-play and Intimacy

When you've enjoyed exploring someone else's body, then it's a good time to continue developing your intimacy – after sex. There's often a time and place for a fling or a quickie but the most amazing sex comes from real intimacy. When you really take the time to get to know someone intimately, at both the emotional and physical levels, that's when you're likely to give them the most pleasure. With increased intimacy comes increased trust. And with trust you'll share the feelings and physical sensations you wouldn't have the courage to share with anyone else.

Continuing the After-play 'Zone'

Enjoying After-play and really being 'in the moment' means not thinking about shopping lists and bills to pay! Why not suggest that you two form a mental image of a 'cocoon' around you both. This cocoon protects you from any outside distractions from the pleasures you've just experienced. If you regularly get into this visual and mental zone (and it's a skill to be practised as with the other visualisation techniques I've highlighted in *Fabulous Foreplay*), you'll learn to switch off from interfering thoughts.

Afterthoughts: Including the Other Things Affecting After-play

The way you feel during seduction, foreplay and sex affects how you feel afterwards. Many men experience an emotional down if they haven't lasted as long as they'd like to. The best suggestion for learning to delay his orgasm, so he can enjoy all the build-up to climax, is to increase his PC muscle strength for staying power. The pubococcygeous muscles (also called the pelvic floor muscles) are those we use to stop ourselves urinating. They are a sling-like set of muscles that both men and women have, supporting the bladder, urethra, rectum and uterus. Once he has identified his

PC muscle he should squeeze it for two to three seconds, and repeat this 10 times. He should build up to exercising the muscles twice a day, with up to 20 repetitions each time.

The Sex Doctor's Prescription For Feeling Fabulous

Once he has built up his PC muscle strength he can start pulsating the muscle just before he reaches his 'point of no return' (the point where he has to ejaculate). By squeezing it just before he gets to orgasm, he slows himself down. She'll love the feel as he pulsates his penis when penetrating her.

Women should also develop their PC muscle strength, as not only will this enhance the strength and duration of orgasms but it will also help prevent bladder weakness. Again, isolate these muscles by squeezing the muscles you would squeeze to stop yourself urinating. Then repeat as per the men's exercises above.

Her Pleasure

No matter how fabulous as a man you might become at foreplay and how much you tease and please a woman's six sexual senses, some women find reaching orgasm difficult. Let me fill you in on one of the best positions for a woman to climax in. It's the CAT – the Coital Alignment Technique. Imagine that she moves to being on top of you in a reverse Missionary Position, with her legs inside of your legs. She then eases upwards so that her clitoral region touches your pubic bone. This creates more tension between your pubic bones and penis, and her vagina.

Once in this position give her 'permission' to control the speed and movement of thrusting. Most women will climax more readily if they're allowed to 'grind' their clitoral region in circular, or back-and-forth motions, against your pubic bone. This will feel good to you because her thighs and vagina will squeeze your penis tightly. Giving her absolute permission to let go and do exactly what feels right to her will also enhance your bond with her.

A Few Surprises For Your Lover's Senses

During foreplay there's nothing wrong – and everything right – with a few surprise tactics. Why not go down on your lover when they least expect it, even before you have both become engrossed in foreplay? Being generous with oral sex demonstrates to your lover that you're not going to be selfish. When you know you two are going to start pleasuring each other, doing something a little out-of-the-blue shows you're happy to spoil them.

Condom Confidence

I mentioned right at the outset that safer sex is your responsibility. But you can turn using condoms into a bit of foreplay. For example, as a man, ask her to slip it on you when aroused. Sometimes this can be a bit daunting, but less so if you've generated trust and respect during foreplay – and if she does fumble a little, you can confidently take over and slip it on with skill. Here are some other condom-confidence tips:

★ Make using condoms more pleasurable by putting a drop of condom-friendly (water-based) lubricant in the tip before slipping it on. This'll make you look like a skilled lover and it'll feel so much better.

★ As with all these things, practice makes perfect – so as a man, when you're on your own masturbating, experiment with slipping condoms on. Enjoy practising!

★ Don't forget that nails and teeth can pierce condoms, so handle them with care.

★ Practise how you approach using a condom with a new lover so that you can suggest using them with confidence. Don't give in to any excuses for not using them. Men, in particular, try things like, 'Don't you think I look clean?' The 'cleanest-looking' person in the world can still have an STI (sexually transmitted infection).

★ Always come back with a confident reply along the lines of, 'I care about both of us and so insist that you wear a condom.'

★ Keep condoms with you at all times – it doesn't make you look cheap; instead it makes you smart.

★ Finally, read the instructions on any new brand of condoms you buy. For example, some are more durable and better for practices such as anal sex.

Good Grooming During Foreplay

A highly erotic grooming technique is to trim each other's pubic hair. What you can do is share a warm shower and then towel each other dry. Take turns trimming each other's pubes. You can gently use your fingers like a comb through his or her pubes as you trim them. Obviously be careful with this technique!

A Change of Scenery

As I pointed out in Chapter 5, on seducing the sexual sense of sight, what you see around you affects how fabulous, or not, your lovemaking is. A change of scenery can do wonders for your sex life, particularly in an established relationship. If you get away for a holiday – even a two-day break – use the sense of freedom that a change of scenery gives you to generate some sexy fantasies. Why not lie beside the pool pretending to be single and ask your partner to chat you up? Then you two can go off for some fun foreplay and even naughty 'stranger sex' where you call each other new, pretend names.

There are lots of little tricks you can use when you're away from your normal surroundings. For example, use delicious, tropical-scented suntan lotions in your hotel room to massage each other sensuously. You could ask her to lie down and drip the lotion slowly down her stomach onto her thighs and then carefully rub it all over her. Or pretend that you're the hotel room-service person who has come in and found her getting out of the shower. Instead of restocking the mini-bar you decide to 'service' all her needs. You could also bring exotic cocktails back to your room, and with the straw, allow some drops to cascade down her breasts for you to lick off – she can do the same to him, dripping the drink down his chest. These little things will stimulate all your senses in fresh ways.

Learn to Let Go

To really get into teasing and pleasing your lover, you need to learn to let go. A couple of tips to try are:

★ Practise making those fabulous 'sex-sounds' on your own, maybe when you're lying in bed pleasuring yourself or are simply enjoying a long, hot shower. This way you'll get used to hearing how you sound and will learn to feel confident letting go around your lover.

★ Get into the moment when you're with your lover and don't get overwhelmed thinking whether or not you're doing something 'right' or 'wrong'. With the huge number of suggestions in the previous chapters, simply pause and check with your lover if something's feeling good – and then just get into it and allow your sixth sense, your intuition, to take over. If you get lost in the moment, your lover will too.

Get Creative and Get out of Your Rut

There are always a few little things you can do to keep things lively in your love life. It's simply about thinking laterally and trying different things. For example, you could forget about going down the gym and instead try one of the new lap-dancing or strip classes that are available for both men and women. Or why not go skinny-dipping at your favourite beauty spot? You could tell your lover you're just going to have a picnic there but bring along finger foods to hand-feed each other and, after feeding each other, strip off for a dip. Always find your 'inner child' when you have the opportunity, perhaps by jumping on the swings in your local park or going down the slide. Carefree fun outside the bedroom can help break down inhibitions during foreplay.

Looking to the Future

You should live in the here and now. And you should also enjoy the little moments with that new person in your life or the person you've loved for a long time. That's a far healthier way to have a relationship than always thinking about what could be better or that the grass is greener elsewhere. Part of this includes doing a few small things to ensure that your future is as loving and sexy as it is now.

✲ Resist sticking to a strict routine in your relationship. Routine is a good and necessary part of life but you should never forego a little spontaneous fun, particularly when it comes to seducing your lover.

✲ Every fortnight or so, you and your lover should switch off your phones and indulge each other in a little quality time.

✲ Use simple items (such as candles, cushions and music) to create a sensual mood in your dining and living areas. People who feel good around each other doing everyday things such as eating, enjoy more sensual and loving relationships.

✲ Surprise your lover occasionally by bringing home something like a new sex toy or a sexy new piece of clothing.

✲ As I mentioned right at the beginning of this book, never forget to flirt with and tease your lover. For example, give them an extra-passionate kiss goodbye in the morning so that they're thinking about it all day.

Final Thoughts

I hope that having read *Fabulous Foreplay*, you're now armed with all sorts of sexy and sensual suggestions that you can use with your lover. By now you should realise there's no right or wrong way to seduce, tease and please someone. Instead, it's about enjoying the moment and creating a fantastic and seductive atmosphere. It's also about being creative in what you do, listening to a lover as well as telling them what you like, and stimulating their six sexual senses and developing yours. And finally, it's about building your own sexual confidence as well as giving each other enough confidence to try new things without feeling at all anxious or fearful.

Enjoy teasing and pleasing your lover even in the smallest ways, so that your foreplay and seduction is truly fabulous!

Dr Pam x

Helpful Numbers

British Pregnancy Advisory Service (BPAS) –
08457 30 40 30

Sexual Health Direct (run by the Family Planning
Association) helpline – 0845 310 1334

The Gender Trust, for help with gender issues –
07000 790347

The Institute of Psychosexual Medicine, for help with
issues of sexuality and gender – 020 7580 0631

Relate Direct, for booking appointments for telephone
counselling – 0845 130 4016

Relateline, Relate's couples and relationship helpline –
0845 130 4010

Sex Addicts Anonymous information line –
020 8946 2436

Sex Wise, for confidential advice – 0800 28 29 30

Websites

Here is a selection of the many adult websites out there. Most of these are straightforward sites selling a range of sex toys and products, though I have added notes for those that offer information, advice or other services. **It is your responsibility to ensure that at the time of use any website is secure.**

Please note that all these websites are prefixed with www.

adameve.com

agentprovocateur.com

amandakiss.co.uk

angelicweapons.co.uk

annsummers.com

athenafem.co.uk – for pelvic muscle exercisers

bedroompleasures.co.uk

blissbox.com

blushingbuyer.co.uk

cherrybliss.com

cliterati.co.uk

coco-de-mer.co.uk

condomania.co.uk

couplebox.com – software to store your private pictures securely

curiosa.co.uk – for erotica

doublydiscreet.com

dreamgirldirect.co.uk

elegantlywaisted.co.uk

emotionalbliss.com

eroticprints.org

erotica-readers.co.uk

eternalspirits.com

femmefun.com

femininezone.com – for information and advice

fetteredpleasures.com

flirtyordirty.co.uk

getmepleasure.co.uk

glamorousamorous.com

goodvibes.com

highestheaven.co.uk

hunkystrippers.com

idlube.co.uk – specialises in lubricants

lovehoney.co.uk

male101.com – about male sexuality

mencorp.com – for strippers

menforalloccasions.com – for escorts

mr-s-leather-fetters.com

myla.com

natural-contours.com

no-angel.com

passion8.com – erotica

pelvictoner.co.uk

pillowtalk.co.uk

scarletmagazine.co.uk – a sexy monthly magazine for women

sda.uk.net – the Sexual Dysfunction Association

serpentstail.com – for hot reading

sexchampionships.com – a sex game to play online

sexplained.com – for information on STIs, etc

sexshop365.co.uk

sextoys.co.uk

sh-womenstore.com

shesaidboutique.com

skintwo.com

slapdat.co.uk – a butt-slapping fun site

slashfic.co.uk – your favourite fictional characters are given hot scenes

takemetobed.co.uk – for erotica and porn

thesexystore.co.uk

whysleep.co.uk

wickedlywildwomen.com

willyworries.com